The DBT Skills and Mindfulness Workbook for Teens

A Dialectical Behavioral Therapy Guide to stop

overthinking, experience anxiety relief,

and master your emotions through

self regulation techniques and practical exercises.

Vivian Foster

TABLE OF CONTENTS

Prize: The Ruby of Protection

Mindfulness and Teens

I: **Complete the Wise Mind Challenge**

Exercise 1: Tapping into the Wise Mind

Exercise 2: Wise Mind Breathing

Exercise 3: Expanding Awareness

Exercise 4: Stone and the Lake

Exercise 5: Questioning if the Wise Mind Is Present

Exercise 6: Focus on the Pause

Exercise 7: Walking Down the Spiral Staircase

II **Complete the WHAT Skills Challenge**

Exercise 8: Hone Your Observational Skills

Exercise 9: Hone Your Description Skills

Exercise 10: Hone Your Participation Skills

Exercise 11: Conduct a Mental Body Scan

Exercise 12: Counting Breaths

Exercise 13: Thought Defusion Exercise: Writing Words in the Sand

Exercise 14: Loving Kindness

III **Complete the HOW Skills Challenge**

Exercise 15: Non-Judgmentally

Exercise 16: One-Mindedly

Exercise 17: Effectively

Section 2

Chapter 4: Take Charge of Your Emotions

Gem: The Sapphire of Emotion in Coron, Palawan

The Sapphire of Emotion

Where Is the Sapphire? Diving Into a Hidden Lagoon in Coron, Palawan

What Is Emotional Regulation?

The Process Model of Emotional Regulation

Something for you...

Dive into a world of possibilities with our **4 Exclusive Audio Guided DBT and Mindfulness Meditations**

Scan the QR Code below to download your copy.

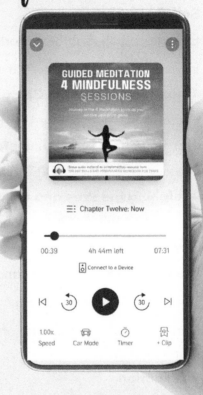

INTRODUCTION

"Being strong doesn't mean that you never break! Being strong means that even if you break into a million pieces, you still have the courage to pick those pieces up, put them back together, and keep going on."

MANPRIT KAUR

Emotions can be incredibly difficult to manage when you're a teen. Adolescence is a wonderful time full of discovery and adventure, but it can also be accompanied by painful, scary emotions that can manifest themselves in anxiety, depression, and suicidal thoughts. Let's take a quick look at some facts that show why the complex world of teen emotions should be taken seriously (World Health Organization 2021).

- On a global level, one in seven ten-to-nineteen-year-olds experiences a mental disorder, accounting for 13 percent of the global burden of disease in this age group.

- The leading causes of illnesses and disability among adolescents are anxiety, depression, and behavioral disorders.

- Suicide is the fourth leading cause of death among 15-to -29-year-olds.

- Failing to address teen mental health conditions as a teen can impair your physical and mental health and limit your chances of leading a happy, fulfilling life when you are an adult.

Of course, anxiety, depression, and self-harm aren't the only problems teens face. Many also struggle with issues like shyness, social anxiety, anger management, and an inability to handle the powerful emotions that overwhelm them, leading to behaviors that can negatively affect their academic, social, and family lives.

Teens aren't lucky enough to have the experience to know that even the toughest emotions—including fear, sadness, frustration, or rejection—will pass. Some may display emotions like anger by bottling it up inside and presenting a calm exterior while they bubble inside. Others may lash out at loved ones, feeling regretful afterward or facing the consequences for their behavior—including shattered friendships and tense family relationships.

Whether you are a parent or a teen, it helps to know that you are not alone—nor is the management of tough emotions a challenge in your home alone. There are powerful physiological reasons teens can find it hard to regulate and negotiate emotions. Arguably, the most influential of these is the fact that the prefrontal cortex (the part of the brain that is responsible for reasoning and emotional regulation) is very much a work in progress. The brain continues to develop and mature until the mid-to-late 20s (National Institute of Mental Health, n.d.). On a positive note, the brain's malleability means teens are ready to learn and adapt to new experiences and situations. You can help strengthen your teen brain by engaging in challenging and creative activities—including exercise, art, and music!

There are other reasons why staying calm and positive can be difficult when things get intense. Because the teen brain is still developing, it can be hard to respond well to stress, making teens more susceptible to stress-related mental conditions like anxiety and depression.

There are also changes taking place in the parts of your brain responsible for social processes. This causes teens to focus more on peer relationships and social experiences, and they may take more risks than they would have in the past, owing to their strong need to belong. Because they are so peer-focused, issues such as arguments with friends, inability to "fit in" at school, and feeling left out by people they admire can feel extremely painful. They may bottle their feelings because they feel ashamed about broaching these subjects with their parents or other trusted family members and friends. If you are a parent and this is happening in your home, know that this doesn't mean your child doesn't trust or appreciate you. Their brains are simply wired to find solutions through their social relationships.

What's more, they are walking the fine line between childhood and adulthood, and they place great pressure on themselves to solve their own problems. The best you can do is let them know you are there if they need to talk. Of course, if they do pour their hearts out to you, then listen; really listen, closing your phone or computer and giving them 100 percent of yourself for as long as they need.

Yet another reason why teens may be a little more irritable or impulsive than in their younger and older years is sleep (or the lack thereof). Research indicates that the sleep hormone melatonin is higher later at night in teens (Nemours Kids Health, n.d.). It also drops later in the morning—which is why teens often find it harder to sleep and wake up early like adults. As a result, they may wake up feeling tired and find it hard to focus and be alert in morning classes.

On the whole, the teen years are ones of transition. The leap between being a kid and getting ready to go off to college to exist on your own is huge but also breathtakingly fast. As you enter high school, everyone seems to expect so much from you—they want you to get good grades, be a good athlete, make and keep friends, and have a large friend group. There are also myriad pressures at school. Everyone wants to be popular, have friends, and be cool, yet this can seem so easy for others yet be painfully difficult for you, particularly if you are shy or self-conscious.

When sad, negative, or angry thoughts take over your mind, you can feel powerless. You may feel tired of "being in your head" and wish you had a special superpower: the ability to rise above your fears and doubts and stop your thoughts from making you unhappy and keeping you stuck in a rut.

If you are a teen, here's a secret you might like to know: even the most confident kids have insecurities, doubts, and pain. They may seem to face disappointments with confidence and bravado, but that doesn't mean they don't have to deal with intense emotions that can be difficult to manage.

Knowing how to deal with tough emotions takes time and experience. More importantly, it involves embracing a small but powerful set of skills that can minimize their impact and maximize your growth—even in the most difficult situations. Dialectical Behavior Therapy (DBT) can help you access these skills swiftly, effectively, and long-lastingly. Consider this book your all-in-one guide for tackling stress, anger, sadness, disappointment, and other intense emotions and becoming stronger and more flexible on the other side of your challenges.

You may not be able to dodge all the curveballs that come your way, but you can learn to catch them, set them aside, and continue to forge your own path. It may take practice, but you will improve in leaps and bounds as you discover your mind's immense power to lead you to a negative or positive state. You are not a passive vessel of your emotions. You very much have a choice as to how you deal with them and how you behave with yourself and others. In case DBT sounds familiar, it's probably because so many well-known people and influencers have spoken about its life-changing effects on them. For instance, Selena Gomez, who struggled with mental issues in her 20s, praised DBT. She stated, "I have this dream of mine that's beyond all of this where I think that personally, it should be required in schools to be taught dialectical behavior therapy." Lady Gaga has also opened up about how DBT is part of her daily mental health regimen.

DBT has helped many people with mental health conditions such as depression. As one proponent of this therapy said, "Before DBT, I felt like the only solution was suicide … through learning various skills from DBT, I can ride the waves of my depression rather than letting them overtake me." Others have stated that although their symptoms haven't gone away, they are much easier to manage thanks to DBT.

This book will guide you through a host of DBT Techniques. Within its pages, you will discover how to:

- *Harness the power of mindfulness.*
- *Be the captain of your own emotions.*
- *Interact with others effectively—even during conflicts and tense situations.*
- *Tolerate distressing situations and emotions instead of trying to repress them.*
- *Nip anxiety in the bud with natural yet highly effective*

stress-busting techniques.

- *Reframe negative thoughts and beliefs standing in the way of your growth, happiness, and relationships.*
- *Control the urge to self-harm.*

You will also have a little fun along the way. You will go on a quest to achieve four priceless gemstones. These gemstones are hidden in mysterious corners of the globe, famed for their beauty and power. Each represents one big step in your journey toward a happy, calm, sociable life.

Nobody said that the teen years were easy. The good news is that despite all the big changes and emotional turmoil that can take place, most teens grow, thrive, and become healthy adults. DBT can be a lifesaver when things get tough, yet one of the most fascinating things about the skills you will harness is that they will be helpful to you throughout your lifetime. As an adult, there will be many occasions in which you will have to deal with intense emotions. If you start practicing DBT as a teen, you will build a mentally strong mind. You will confidently know that no matter how hard life gets, you—and only you—are the captain of your emotions.

What are you waiting for, then? Let's get started on the adventure of a lifetime!

CHAPTER 1

What is DBT and

How can it transform your life

"Acceptance can transform, but if you accept in order to transform, it is not acceptance. It is like loving. Love seeks no reward, but when given freely comes back a hundred-

MARSHA M. LINEHAN

By now, you're probably keen to begin your quest for the first gem. We will take a brief pause to make sure you are 100 percent ready for the exciting challenges ahead. In this chapter, we will discover what DBT is and why it is so effective at helping you deal with intense emotions. Knowing exactly why you are undertaking specific activities or completing worksheets is vital. To do so, it helps to understand how DBT developed and its primary purpose.

What is DBT and How does it differ from CBT?

Dialectical Behavioral Therapy, or DBT, is based on another "gold standard" therapy called Cognitive-Behavioral Therapy (CBT). Like DBT, CBT is used to tackle a myriad of mental health issues, including stress, anxiety, and depression. CBT is based on the idea that thoughts, emotions, and behavior all influence each other. For instance, if you think negatively about a situation, it can lead you to have negative emotions. These emotions can then lead you to adopt behaviors that may stand in the way your goals and your overall happiness.

The idea behind CBT is to enact vital changes that can make you feel more positive about life and eliminate the obstacles to your goals. CBT helps you recognize when your thoughts might become troublesome and gives you techniques to redirect those thoughts. DBT helps you find ways to accept yourself, feel safe, and manage your emotions to regulate potentially destructive or harmful behaviors. Although DBT is essentially a type of CBT, it has two added elements:

It is particularly efficient at dealing with intense emotions because it empowers you to accept them as they are without allowing them to take over. DBT teaches you to "ride out" difficult emotions instead of pushing them away or turning to unhealthy outlets to mask pain or discomfort (Cleveland Clinic, n.d.).

A Brief History of DBT—Marsha's Story

DBT was developed by American psychologist and author Marsha Linehan, who, in her youth, battled against severe mental illness. At the age of 17, Marsha was the sole occupant of a "seclusion room" for mentally ill patients. She attacked herself frequently and had a profound urge to end her life. She knew she was out of control but says she had "no way to communicate what was going on, no way to understand it." (Carey 2011).

Marsha was diagnosed with schizophrenia, dosed with a host of powerful drugs, and given electroshock treatments. She was discharged from the hospital in 1963 after a 26-month stay. Despite her ordeal, she never lost sight of her passion: helping others.

In 1967, after a couple of suicide attempts, she took a job as a clerk in an insurance company while she studied for her degree. She often prayed at a chapel, and one day, while doing so, she had what she called a "shimmering experience." She says, "I just ran back to my room and said, 'I love myself.' It was the first time I remember talking to myself in the first person. I felt transformed."

Sadly, her happiness was short-lived. She felt devastated once again after a romance ended. However, she realized that one important thing had changed: she could experience the pain without wanting to harm herself.

Her studies in psychology helped (she obtained a Ph.D. at Loyola University), though her own experiences were also key in helping her understand why she had been unable to withstand her pain in the past. The reason was the enormous gap between her current life and the life she wanted to lead. She concluded that the answer to dealing with this conundrum was "radical acceptance." Her studies in behavioralism taught her that by changing the way you behave, you can also change the way you think and feel about things. However, she added a second component into the equation: acceptance. By accepting life as it is (instead of continuing to wish it were different), you can change it for the better. It sounded contradictory, but it wasn't—and she soon put her theory to the test.

As a professional, Marsha focused on treating patients with borderline personality disorder—the diagnosis she would have given herself when she was younger. This disorder manifested itself in outbursts, self-destruction, and neediness. She found that these patients needed validation and acceptance. Marsha accepted that their behaviors (even their destructive ones) made some sense because they felt emotions like rage, anxiety, and emptiness so much more intensely than the average person. However, DBT was not only focused on acceptance; it also had to incorporate change because her patients wanted to change for the better. They didn't want to stay stuck in the same rut. Today, she asks her patients to commit to change because there is no point in feeling down in the dumps for longer than you have to—and that means doing something different!

Her method, DBT, involved using a small set of techniques in day -to-day life that would make difficult emotions more manageable. These techniques included taking the opposite action to what your instincts tell you and mindfulness meditation—observing your thoughts and emotions without judgement and watching them come and go without trying to fight against them or repress them.

Marsha's experiments had excellent results, with various studies showing that patients who had undergone DBT had lower suicide and hospitalization rates. They were also more likely to remain in treatment. Today, DBT is used for many conditions, including eating disorders and substance abuse. However, its tenets are helpful for everyone—not only those who struggle with stress, anxiety, depression, and triggering situations. Interestingly, Marsha says that to this day, she still has ups and downs, though she is happier when she thinks of the millions of people she has helped across the globe.

For what is DBT used?

DBT is a popular treatment for the following conditions (Schimelpfening 2023):

- attention-deficit/hyperactivity disorder (ADHD)
- bipolar disorder
- borderline personality disorder (BPD)
- eating disorders (such as anorexia nervosa, binge-eating disorder, and bulimia nervosa)
- generalized anxiety disorder (GAD)
- major depressive disorder (including treatment-resistant major depression and chronic depression)
- non-suicidal self-injury
- obsessive-compulsive disorder (OCD)
- post-traumatic stress disorder (PTSD)
- substance use disorder
- suicidal behavior

However, you don't have to be diagnosed with a mental health condition to harness the benefits of the many DBT techniques you will discover in this book.

What are the benefits of DBT?

DBT can help with six main points (Schimelpfening 2023):

1. **Acceptance and Change**: Learn to tolerate your circumstances, emotions and self, and how to develop skills you need to make positive changes in your behaviors and interactions with others.
2. **Behavioral Issues:** Begin to analyze problematic or destructive behavioral patterns so you can replace them with healthier ones.
3. **Cognitive Issues:** Practice challenging thoughts and beliefs that are ineffective or unhelpful.

4. **Collaboration:** Learn to communicate effectively.

5. **Skill Sets:** Engage in new skill sets to enhance your capabilities.

6. **Support:** Recognize your positive strengths and attributes and use them to full advantage.

The 4 Sections of DBT

DBT has four main sections or components. In this book, each section will represent one challenge. The sections are (DBTSelfHelp.com, n.d.):

1 Mindfulness:

This section draws your brain's focus to the present moment so you can slow down life and achieve inner peace. When you aren't running over past events in your head or worrying about the future, you can focus more on "the here and now."

2 Distress Tolerance:

This section seeks to help you find ways to deal with emotional incidents without feeling overwhelmed. It enhances your ability to "bounce back" to a peaceful state after stressors, negative thoughts, and intense emotions.

3 Interpersonal Skills:

To get along with others, you must display interpersonal skills such as being empathetic, being a good listener, and communicating your wants and needs assertively.

4 Emotional Regulation:

The goal of this section is to help you manage your emotions instead of being managed by them, as well as to reduce your vulnerability to negative emotions and build positive experiences.

Mindfulness and distress tolerance are "acceptance skills," while emotional regulation and interpersonal effectiveness are "change skills."

How This Book Works

This book takes you on an exciting adventure as you discover more about yourself and start taking your emotions by the reins. At the beginning of each chapter, you will be introduced to a mysterious corner of the world where a gem symbolizing a personal goal is hidden. To obtain the gem, you will be asked to complete the challenge posed at the beginning of the section.

Each section will be divided into two chapters (or "tasks"). The first chapter will provide a theoretical explanation regarding the section, and the second will contain worksheets and activities that will enable you to start applying the DBT skills you have learned about in the previous chapter.

After completing each two-task challenge, the gem will be yours. You will then complete a mindfulness meditation script centered around this gem.

Now that you know what DBT is and how it can help you, it's time to complete the first section: Mindfulness. You will carry out a host of activities, so put your thinking cap on and get ready for your first step in this adventure!

SECTION 1

CHAPTER 2

Mindfulness: Embrace The Wonder of Now

GEM: The Ruby of Protection in Son Doong Cave

"Mindfulness is one of those things you simply do because if you practice being aware—completely open to the universe; just exactly as it is — you will transform your life in time."

MARSHA M. LINEHAN

Your goal in Section 1 (Chapters 2 and 3) will be to find the Ruby of Protection by harnessing the superpower of mindfulness—keeping your mind in the present moment. In this chapter, you will discover what mindfulness is. Next, in Chapter 3, you will get straight to work, completing exercises and worksheets so you can learn to accept your thoughts and emotions without judging them.

The Ruby of Protection

The ruby is a gem that ancient warriors in Burma and China used to adorn their armor to protect them in battle (American Gem Society, n.d.). This is because the ruby is an extremely strong stone! It ranks 9 on the Mohs scale of mineral hardness, placing it directly under the diamond (which ranks an impressive and perfect 10/10!).

It takes bravery to approach your problems mindfully because when you feel intense emotions like anger or sadness, the tendency is to run away from or repress them, pretending they don't exist. Of course, when you do so, your emotions can bubble up, and you can "explode," saying or doing things that you regret later.

Approaching your thoughts and emotions mindfully involves accepting them just as they are without judging them. In order to do so, courage, compassion, and love are required, and loving yourself unconditionally can be one of the hardest things you will be called upon to do throughout your lifetime!

Let this ruby symbolize your ability to bravely face your emotions and "give yourself to the here and now," knowing that your thoughts and emotions are temporary. They do not define you, and they can intensify, wane, change, and even disappear over time.

The Ruby of Protection

The ruby is a gem that ancient warriors in Burma and China used to adorn their armor to protect them in battle. This is because the ruby is an extremely strong stone! It ranks 9 on the Mohs scale of mineral hardness, placing it directly under the diamond (which ranks an impressive and perfect 10/10!).

It takes bravery to approach your problems mindfully because when you feel intense emotions like anger or sadness, the tendency is to run away from or repress them, pretending they don't exist. Of course, when you do so, your emotions can bubble up, and you can "explode," saying or doing things that you regret later.

Let this ruby symbolize your ability to bravely face your emotions and "give yourself to the here and now," knowing that your thoughts and emotions are temporary. They do not define you, and they can intensify, wane, change, and even disappear over time. Mindfulness takes practice, but the effort you invest is well worth it. Mindfulness is, without doubt, one of the most powerful allies you will have when it comes to winning your battle over even the most difficult, painful, and challenging situations, words, and emotions.

Mindfulness takes practice, but the effort you invest is well worth it. Mindfulness is, without doubt, one of the most powerful allies you will have when it comes to winning your battle over even the most difficult, painful, and challenging situations, words, and emotions.

Where Is the Ruby? Climbing into Son Doong Cave in Vietnam

To find this priceless gem, you will be mentally trekking into the virgin jungle of the Son Doong Cave in Vietnam—the largest cave in the world (Edström, n.d.). This cave measures over 5.5 miles in length, and some of its caverns are large enough to hold a 40-story skyscraper. Deep within this cave is a lush jungle growing more than 600 feet beneath the Earth's surface. It that enters the cave through a part of the roof that has collapsed. This jungle has plants of all sizes and trees that grow up to 100 feet tall! A river also flows within this cave. Waiting for you by the rocks at the base of a stalagmite in this cave called the Hand of the Dog is the

Scan to see the magnificient location

What Is the Mindfulness Superpower

You may have heard of mindfulness or even participated in a mindfulness meditation session or two at school. In the DBT world, mindfulness is considered the core component of emotional regulation—the ability to control your emotional state.

The Son Doong Cave

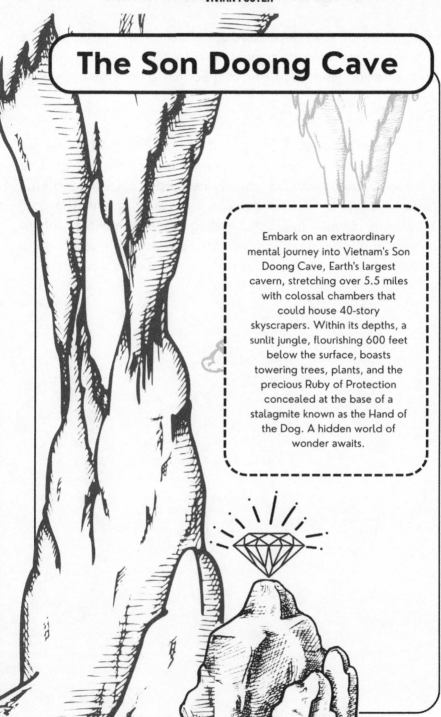

Embark on an extraordinary mental journey into Vietnam's Son Doong Cave, Earth's largest cavern, stretching over 5.5 miles with colossal chambers that could house 40-story skyscrapers. Within its depths, a sunlit jungle, flourishing 600 feet below the surface, boasts towering trees, plants, and the precious Ruby of Protection concealed at the base of a stalagmite known as the Hand of the Dog. A hidden world of wonder awaits.

All the other DBT skills depend to some extent on mindfulness, so it is the first task you must complete to stop intense emotions from controlling your state of mind (Cognitive Behavioral Therapy Los Angeles, n.d.).

So, what is mindfulness? Think of it as the ability to recognize when your mind is caught up in thought and to draw it back to the present experience. DBT mindfulness adds something a little special to this process: mindfulness without judgment. The goal is to attend to your thoughts, feelings, and behaviors without rejecting or invalidating your emotions—since this leads to a persistent loss of emotional control.

Daily Mindfulness Challenges

It may all sound pretty simple, but people actually spend very little time in the present moment. It is very easy for our minds to wander (Kam 2017). On some days, you may physically be in one place while thinking of a previous discussion with someone else—running the argument over and over again in your head. Many people also worry about the future—an upcoming test, upcoming expenses, or a social occasion you are worried about attending.

The following situations display a wandering mind at play:

You are in the family car with your dad, talking about an upcoming plan you have together. As your dad starts to give you the details, your mind wanders to a conversation you had with a classmate. By the time you arrive at your destination, you don't recall any of the details your dad explained to you in the car.

You're in class, and your math teacher is explaining a problem on the whiteboard. However, you notice that your friend is telling someone else a joke a few seats down, and you wish you knew what they were saying. When the teacher finishes and asks you to complete an exercise, you realize you don't know where to start.

You're doing homework at home, but you keep stopping to watch your favorite YouTube influencer. You tell yourself you will keep your break to five minutes but soon realize you've been watching YouTube for an hour. It's too late to finish, so you leave your homework undone.

You are trying to resolve an argument with your friend, but while they are talking, you are simply thinking of what you want to say in response. You start recalling other situations where they did something that hurt you, and you are trying to remember these in detail so you can blurt it out as soon as they pause to take a breath.

You are playing a game with your little sister, but your mind keeps wondering why someone in your class threw a party and invited everyone in your friend group except for you. You begin to recall moments you shared with this person and cannot figure out why they haven't invited you. You end your play session with your sibling because you become overwhelmed by the feeling of rejection.

You have been battling depression for a while, and you cannot stop engaging in your own thoughts about your problems and negative experiences, even when you are having a meal with family members. Everyone is laughing and having a good time, but you seem far away from the moment.

Is Mind Wandering Always a Negative Thing?

Mind wandering isn't, per se, a negative thing. There are good things that can result from this activity. For instance, one thing you may do when your mind wanders is to plan for the future. Planning ahead is a good use of time because it allows you to efficiently carry out your day-to-day tasks, such as getting to and from school, finishing your homework on time, and doing something you promised for a friend. When your mind wanders, you can also reflect on how you behaved in a specific situation and think about what you could have done differently to improve the outcome.

However, on some occasions—when a difficult or triggering situation arises—it is vital to exercise mental discipline and keep our minds in the present. When something happens that results in negative thoughts and emotions, we need to do two things: first, we need to be aware of the thoughts going through our minds. Second, we need to practise mindfulness so that we can stay in control of these emotions rather than letting them control us.

DBT and Emotional Dysregulation

Earlier, we mentioned that DBT can help you with emotional regulation (or managing your emotions). DBT targets emotional dysregulation—which occurs when you cannot manage your own emotional states. For instance, you may sometimes feel so overtaken by sadness, anger, or guilt that you get into a cycle of negative thinking or "explode" and raise your voice at others. Afterward, you may find returning to your usual, calm state very hard.

The truth is that there is no way to avoid challenges, and they can occur almost daily from the moment you leave your home.

For instance, you may be in a car with a parent and get caught in a traffic jam; this may "make your blood boil" when you know you have to be in class early because you have an exam. At school, someone can say an unkind comment that fills you with self-doubt and self-loathing, and you may struggle to feel more upbeat and positive or enjoy your friends that day in their joyful banter. After school, you may have football or swim practice, and your results may be worse than they were the week before. You can feel incredibly angry at yourself or look for someone to blame—your coach, the person who was unkind to you that day, the traffic jam that got you flustered for the first time that day. The good news is that you don't need to stay "locked" in these thought processes and emotional states. You can take steps to be the master of your own mind through DBT.

SIGNS OF EMOTIONAL DYSREGULATION

Typical signs of emotional dysregulation include (Jelinek 2022):

 MOOD SHIFTS

Bursting into tears or feeling upset without a clear reason for it

 PERFECTIONISM

Disordered eating

 RELATIONSHIP CONFLICTS

Finding it hard to deal with stress

 ANGRY OUT BURSTS

High anxiety

 DEPRESSION

Feelings of shame

 SUICIDAL THOUGHTS OR ACTIONS

How Emotional Dysregulation Can Harm You

Emotional dysregulation can cause you to respond by (Yeung 2023):

1. **Fighting**: You may scream and yell or otherwise lash out at others. You do so to protect yourself as if you were defending yourself against imminent danger. The problem with emotional dysregulation is that it can cause you to lash out in situations where you aren't actually in any imminent danger. Usually, problems can be resolved much more effectively by communicating with others calmly and assertively.

2. **Fleeing:** You may feel like running away, and that is exactly what you may do. Instead of discussing any issues you have with someone else, you may suddenly escape the scene, leaving others feeling hurt or annoyed. Another form of fleeing is ghosting—making yourself unavailable by not answering texts or calls or avoiding someone for several days. If you've been ghosted before, you know how painful and frustrating it can be.

3. **Freezing:** Emotions can be so intense that they can make you freeze in the spot, incapable of articulating your wants and needs.

4. **Fawning:** You may immediately say or do things to please others and avoid any conflict. Even though you know that you are right and even if you feel like others are crossing your boundaries, you may give in and do or say what they want. It may feel good at the moment (since tensions are reduced), but afterward, you can feel angry at yourself for prioritizing everyone's wants and needs except your own. In doing so, you send the message that you have no boundaries and do not count in the relationship. In fact, healthy relationships have boundaries, and they value both party's wants, needs, and emotions. They involve a healthy amount of give and take.

All the above behaviors are the result of your body responding to threats. These responses can have short-term benefits, but think of how self-defeating they can be.

Sometimes, your body enters these states even when there is no threat present, resulting in anxiety, depression, or difficulties controlling your emotional responses. Dysregulation pushes you beyond your window of tolerance—the state where you can manage your emotions and not become overwhelmed by stress.

DBT Turns Mindfulness into a Superpower

Through DBT, you can harness the superpower of mindfulness—a practice that allows you to recognize and accept unpleasant emotions without making judgments. Fully engaging in what you are doing in a given moment leaves little room for negative attributions. Mindfulness can help you (Cognitive Behavioral Therapy Los Angeles, n.d.).

Avoid a downward spiral.

Make the best decisions, and ensure your wants and needs are validated.

Give up your struggle against painful emotions. You can't argue with emotion! Especially if you accept each one fully and unconditionally. Paradoxically, acceptance is one of the most powerful ways to reduce the sting of painful emotions or make them go away!

Mindfulness as a Challenge

In the next chapter, you will jump straight into challenges that will help you hone your ability to remain in the present. Know that mindfulness can be difficult at first because our brains are hardwired NOT to be mindful. We are used to making judgments, "time traveling," and creating stories in our heads. In a way, mindfulness works against your brain biology. Therefore, don't expect perfection! Mindfulness takes practice. The more you try it out, the easier it becomes to recognize when your mind is going to dangerous places and to take the steps to ensure you are always the master of your own

CHAPTER 3

Complete the Wise Mind and WHAT Skills Challenge PRIZE: The Ruby of Protection

"Willingness is listening very carefully to your Wise Mind, and then acting from your Wise Mind."

MARSHA M. LINEHAN

Now that you know what mindfulness is and how you can harness its benefits when situations are challenging or intense, you are ready to take on 3 separate challenges—the Wise Mind, WHAT Skills, and HOW Skills challenges. In case you need a bit more inspiration, however, let's briefly discuss a few benefits that mindfulness has for teens in particular.

Mindfulness and Teens

Numerous studies have been carried out on the effect of mindfulness on the teen brain and aspects such as stress and mood. These studies have revealed that:

- Mindfulness, the process of learning to become more aware of one's ongoing experiences and present state, boosts well-being in teen boys. Specifically, it helps them feel positive emotions (such as happiness, interest, and affection) and function well (Huppert and Johnson 2010.).

- Mindfulness at school reduces the likelihood of having symptoms of depression in adolescence (Raes et al. 2013).

- Mindfulness is a powerful tool when it comes to improving emotional disorders and psychological problems in adolescents (Tang et al. 2021).

I: Complete the Wise Mind Challenge

"Wise Mind" is a phrase coined by DBT's founder, Marsha M. Linehan. She espoused that it lies somewhere between the emotional mind (making decisions and judgments based entirely on your emotions) and the reasonable mind (when your thoughts, decisions, and judgments are based entirely on facts and rational thinking).

Examples of your emotional mind at work would be the

- You always do well in English and are particularly good at writing. However, while working on a group project, a classmate tells you your writing is boring. You get very emotional and start believing what they have said. You try to imagine what they mean when they say your writing should be more "dynamic," and you get blocked up. You end up not writing what you initially intended and asking someone else to take over. Your group does not get the grade you hoped you would, and you feel that if you had done your share, you would have obtained a better result.

- You usually plan your weekends, but one Friday, your friend calls you up and tells you they have an extra ticket to see your favorite rap artist. You get super excited and say yes, even though you haven't planned all the details yet.

- You see a cute puppy at the park and cannot help but call it to you to pet it. You feel an instant sense of bliss when it snuggles up against you and gives you kisses.

- You are at a clothes shop, and you're tired and stressed because you have to get back home to do your homework. The salesperson is not very friendly, and you snap at them, then feel bad about it later.

- Your best friend looks busy when you approach them to share some news. Without stopping to think about what you're doing, you accuse them of being rude and selfish and only being nice when they want your attention. They get angry right back, and you don't talk to each other for days.

As you see, the emotional mind has some wonderful aspects to it, but if you allow it to take over all the time, you could suffer negative consequences that take quite some time and effort to fix.

Examples of your rational mind at work:

- You are taking the subway while you're traveling with family. You check out the pertinent lines and times beforehand and confidently know where to go when you arrive at the station.

- You have an upcoming test, and you start studying a couple of weeks in advance, dividing the number of topics you need to learn into a specific number of days so you are fully prepared when the test comes around.

- You buy a school supply you need on the way to school because you know the store will be closed in the afternoon.

- You decide to learn a new language because your research has shown that it can help you get a better job when you are older.

- You plan your next birthday party, including the food, music, and games.

Your rational mind helps you be logical and reasonable about what is happening. When in rational mode, you analyze things and base your decisions on observation or experimentation. Thinking rationally is rare, and it can come in handy when emotions are tense. However, when people are in rational mode, they can sometimes come across as cold. On the contrary, you may have met someone who seemed kind, friendly, and warm. Perhaps it is because they were using their "wise mind."

Think of the wise mind as a marriage of your emotional and rational sides. It's a bit like having the best of both worlds, as your heart and mind are in congruence (Attai 2020). It is deeply intuitive and at play when, for instance, you pursue a healthy and loving relationship or a passion that looks and feels right. Take a look at the following graph, which represents the nature of the wise mind:

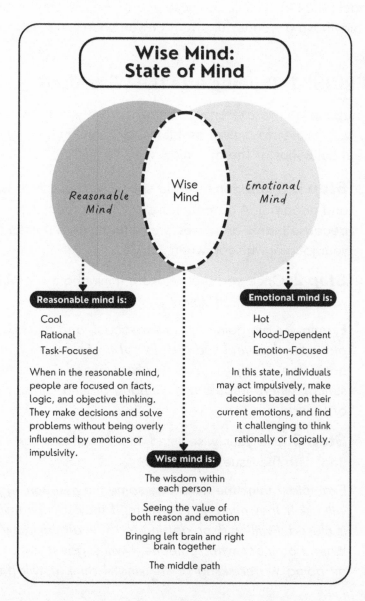

Wise Mind: State of Mind

Reasonable Mind

Wise Mind

Emotional Mind

Reasonable mind is:

Cool

Rational

Task-Focused

When in the reasonable mind, people are focused on facts, logic, and objective thinking. They make decisions and solve problems without being overly influenced by emotions or impulsivity.

Emotional mind is:

Hot

Mood-Dependent

Emotion-Focused

In this state, individuals may act impulsively, make decisions based on their current emotions, and find it challenging to think rationally or logically.

Wise mind is:

The wisdom within each person

Seeing the value of both reason and emotion

Bringing left brain and right brain together

The middle path

Now that you are very clear on what the wise mind is, how about completing a few exercises focusing on how to attain it? You will see that it is easier than you may think, as it is so intuitive, and it simply encourages you to tap into tools that already exist in your mind. You don't have to do all these exercises every day. Simply practise each and turn to those that work best for you. Go back once in a while to those you find more challenging, as they may have a wonderful effect on you once you master them.

EXERCISE 1: Tapping into the Wise Mind

The purpose of this exercise is simply to get you used to using your wise mind to solve problems or conflicts in your life (Dialectical Behavior Therapy, n.d.).

Step 1: Find a comfortable spot. Try to ensure it is quiet and peaceful. A garden, park, or other green spot is ideal because plants and trees are natural stress busters. Bring your journal with you when you go.

Step 2: Once you feel relaxed, think about a problem in your life and write it down.

Example: I am going to a new school, and the kids make plans for the weekend but do not invite me. As a result, I am often lonely on the weekends, and I miss my old school, where I could always hang around with my group of friends.

Step 3: Use your wise mind to think of a smart way to deal with the issue.

Example: I think the next time someone mentions a plan, I will ask if they mind if I join them. If they say the invitation is closed, I will work on getting to know others in my class. When I connect with someone, I will suggest a plan, such as going water skiing or trekking. I think it will help if I have exciting suggestions of my own instead of waiting for others to propose a plan.

Step 4: Write down how you feel after the exercise.

Example: I feel glad that I am taking steps to change what I am unhappy about. Instead of just feeling bad about being alone and focusing on others' behavior, I am focusing on the steps I can take to make myself feel better.

EXERCISE 2: Wise Mind Breathing

This exercise is a handy way to calm down when thoughts or emotions threaten to overwhelm you (Tasmanian Suicide Prevention Community Network, n.d.). It's this easy:

- Breathe in with a slow, big breath, and as you inhale, say the word "Wise."

- Exhale, taking time to do so. As you say the word "Mind."

    Repeat this various times until you notice you are calmer. You may notice that your heart rate has gone down and that you no longer need to blurt out your emotions without thinking or escaping from your situation. When you are fully calm, you can find a peaceful spot and try to resolve any difficulties you have encountered by using your wise mind.

EXERCISE 3: Expanding Awareness

This breathing exercise is excellent for bringing your mind to the present moment (Tasmanian Suicide Prevention Community Network, n.d.). Breathing also helps you relax and reduce your heart rate if it is racing because of stress or anxiety.

1. Find a comfortable spot and sit or lie down, closing your eyes gently.

2. Breathe in and focus your awareness on your center.

3. Breathe out and expand your awareness to your surroundings.

4. Stay in the moment and repeat the exercise as many times as you need to.

EXERCISE 4: Stone and the Lake

This exercise invites you to imagine that you are a stone. The aim is to help you attain a sense of centeredness, focus, and calm (Tasmanian Suicide Prevention Community Network, n.d.).

Imagine that it is a beautiful, sunny day. You are a small, flat, smooth stone lying on the ground by a serene lake with clear, sparkling water. Someone picks you up and tosses you in the water. You imagine that you are gently arching your way through the water until you reach your destination, and you begin to make your way to the bottom of the lake.

Imagine yourself gently making your way to the bottom. Perhaps you are doing so in a circular motion or backward and forward. When you reach the bottom, focus your attention right there, within yourself.

Notice how peaceful the lake is. Notice how quiet and serene you feel. Nothing and no one is bothering you, and you are reaching an optimal state of calm.

Travel to the center of yourself and remain there for a while.

EXERCISE 5: Questioning if the Wise Mind is Present

This exercise is excellent for reminding you to use the wise mind. The next time you think a thought, plan something, or decide to take a course of action, ask yourself, "Is this the wise mind?" (Tasmanian Suicide Prevention Community Network, n.d.).

Breathe in and listen for the answer. Do not tell yourself the answer; just listen for it and wait until it comes to you.

Keep asking with each breath you take. Do not force the answer. If you have to take several breaths until it comes, then do so calmly.

EXERCISE 6: Focus on the Pause

Like many mindfulness-based exercises, this one also involves breathing. Once again, the aim is to bring your mind to the present and to stop thoughts and emotions from leading you to a flustered or negative state (Tasmanian Suicide Prevention Community Network, n.d.).

> *Breathe in and focus on the pause. Breathe out and focus on the pause. With each pause, allow yourself to travel to the central space within the pause.*

EXERCISE 7: Walking Down the Spiral Staircase

The aim of this exercise is to empower you to travel to the center of yourself (CRAFT Connect, n.d.). When you hone this task, you can recognize and respect your feelings when you are undergoing tough experiences. You can respond to your thoughts and emotions in ways that are loving and non-judgmental.

> *Get into a comfortable position in a chair or on the floor. If you are seated, place both your feet on the floor and take a couple of deep breaths, becoming aware of the air entering and leaving your lungs.*
>
> *Next, imagine that there is a spiral staircase within you. Make the staircase as light or dark as you wish, and add as many windows as you'd like.*
>
> *Take a slow walk down to the center of yourself—within this center are your wisdom and wise mind. As you do so, try to notice if you are tired or afraid. Pause if you feel tired, and keep going when you have caught your breath.*

When you arrive at a still point, stop and sit down.

When you are ready, open your eyes and take a couple of deep breaths. Try to maintain the awareness of that wise center within you.

Try to practice this exercise three times a week so you can efficiently get to your calm center when you need to. That way, when you encounter a challenging situation in the future, you can ask to be excused and go to a calm spot. Once you're there, you can access the spiral staircase, travel down to your core wisdom, and make a decision that represents the union of your emotional and rational minds.

II: Complete the WHAT SKILLS Challenge

WHAT skills are the second component of mindfulness in DBT. These practical skills help you take control and have a "Teflon" or "no-stick" mind in the face of intense situations. By relying on them, you can allow experiences, feelings, and thoughts to come into your mind and slip right out. That way, your mind doesn't get stuck in a negative moment and become overwhelmed by negative thoughts and emotions. Your goal isn't to fight tough thoughts and emotions or push them away but rather to attend to them while still remaining in the driver's seat. There are three WHAT skills to sharpen:

WHAT Skills

WHAT skills are the second component of mindfulness in DBT. These practical skills help you take control and have a "Teflon" or "no-stick" mind in the face of intense situations.

There are three WHAT skills to sharpen:

Observe

Notice your bodily sensations. For instance, if you are stressed, you may notice that your heart is beating faster, that your skin goes red and feels hot, and that you start taking in shorter, faster breaths.

Pay purposeful attention to the present moment.

Controle your attention, but not what you see. The aim is to avoid pushing away thoughts and emotions but also to not cling to them. They simply exist, and you recognize them without judging them.

Practice wordless watching. See the thoughts come into your mind and let them go by like moving clouds. Notice your feelings rising and falling like waves in the ocean.

Observe what is taking place within and what is taking place outside yourself as well.

Describe

Name your experiences. For instance, if someone says something hurtful or offensive, you might say, "I am feeling very angry," or "My knees are weakening," or "My stomach is tightening."

Label what you are observing. Label a thought as just a thought. Do the same for feelings and actions.

Answer the four "Wh" questions without interpreting them or forming an opinion of them. Simply describe the "Who, What, When, and Where" that is taking place. Keep it to the facts.

For example:
Who did this involve? "It involved my friend Henry." What happened? "He made fun of my prom dress." When? "This evening." Where? "At the dance hall."

Remember that in order to describe the experience, you need to observe it through your senses.

Participate

Immerse yourself completely in what is going on in the present. For instance, if you are in a hip-hop class, your goal is to keep your mind right there, concentrating on the music, the steps, and how you feel when you're dancing. The same goes for whatever activity you carry out—reading, cleaning, or conversing with a friend.

Unite yourself with whatever you are doing. Forget yourself and give your full attention to what you are doing.

Act intuitively, using your wise mind. Think of how a skillful guitarist can jam or improvise to the music or how a dancer intuitively moves their body with grace when the music starts. Try to give yourself this way, using your intuition, to enjoy the moment. Don't force it or avoid it; just be at one with it.

Go with the flow. Take part in the moment with spontaneity.

EXERCISE 6: Hone Your Observational Skills

The aim of this exercise is to use your senses to observe what is taking place within or without (Kaiser Permanente, n.d.).

 Observe with your EYES.

There are many ways to use your eyes to observe your surroundings. The following can inspire you to start doing so today:

- Lie on the ground in a park and watch the clouds move.

- In the park, try to identify all the different plants, flowers, and trees you encounter. Notice the subtle differences in color and shape, and notice where in the park the sunlight is shining. Study the way the park is laid out—where the walkways, benches, and trees are. See how many shady areas there are and what spots would make a nice setting for a picnic.

- Sit outside a café and watch the people go by. Do not follow them with your head or eyes; just let them "flow" by.

- Focus on one aspect of your pet or of a person in your home; it could be their mouth, eyes, nose, or any other part of their face.

- Pick up a flower and try to notice all its tiny details. You can do this with anything that is beautiful or fascinates you.

Observe with your EARS.

- Head to a park, green area, or seaside and listen carefully to all the sounds you hear. It could be birds chirping, the sound of leaves rustling beneath your feet, or people laughing in the distance.

- If someone is talking, pay close attention to all the aspects of their speech—including the speed at which they talk, the volume, the pauses between their words, and similar.

- Listen to a song you like and try to observe the way the singer changes their voice. Does it sometimes sound more metallic or raspy and smoother or more melodic at other times? Is their voice more breathy or more forceful in the specific song you are listening to? Also, notice the different instruments and the tone they add to the song. Listen to the lyrics and try to find a meaning from them that may apply to your life.

- Choose a sound that makes you feel calm. It could be a recording of waves, nature, or the rain. Try to breathe along to its rhythm. Close your eyes and tune into the sound after you finish listening to it. Recall this sound (and how you breathed along to it) when a distraction happens.

- Take a bell and strike it (or clang a pair of mini cymbals) to create a tone, listening to the sound until it is completely gone.

Observe with your sense of TASTE.

- Play a fun blindfolded taste testing session, asking someone in your family to prepare around six different snacks, each with a different texture. As you taste each snack, take time to notice how it feels on your tongue, its smoothness or crunch, and what it feels like when you bite into or swallow it.

- Lick a lollipop or another food and notice the sensation of taste on your tongue.

- Bite into crunchy, juicy, or crisp foods, noticing the sensation that each texture produces.

 Observe with your sense of SMELL.

- Take one or two colognes or perfumes and research their notes (top notes, main notes, and base notes) online. Spray the fragrance on your wrist and try to see if you can identify the notes you have discovered.

- Cook something fragrant. One very simple but fragrant dish is boiled apples. Slice an apple and cover it slightly with water, a little brown sugar, and a cinnamon stick. It will take just a few minutes for your apples to become soft, but in the meantime, enjoy the deliciously warm, spicy, and festive fragrance that fills your home.

 Observe with your sense of TOUCH.

- Run something soft across your lips, like a soft cloth or a feather.

- When you're walking, notice the sensation of your feet

hitting the ground and rising up. Walk slowly, then fast, and notice the difference. If you live in a beachy area, walk along the seashore and notice the difference between walking on dry sand (far from the shore) and on wet sand (closer to the shore). Which takes more effort, and which feels more pleasurable

- Place one hand on something cold and the other on something hot, and notice the difference.

- Do the dishes by hand, noticing how the hot water, suds, and sponge feel on your hands. Feel each dish or glass as you wash it.

 ### Engage all your senses.

Head to a beautiful spot, such as a green area or the beach. Go for a place with beautiful natural features such as plants, water, birds, etc. Notice what you see, feel, hear, and smell. Touch different textures in this area—such as plants and flowers, the ground, sand, tree barks, and similar.

 ### Give yourself fully to the present moment.

Notice every sense you are aware of, then make "reciprocal statements such as "I smell the flower, the flower smells me." "I see the plant, the plant sees me," and "I hear the music, the music hears me."

 ### Observe thoughts and emotions

When a thought comes to your mind, say it to yourself. For instance, "The thought 'that girl is looking at you' is arising within me." Try the same with your emotions. For instance, "A feeling of rage is arising within me," or "A feeling of elation is arising within me."

Observe painful thoughts.

- When you have painful thoughts, imagine that each is a cloud. Watch the clouds go by without judging them or trying to make them go away faster than they are.

- Imagine that each thought is a person passing by a palace. You are the guard, and you calmly watch them walk past.

EXERCISE 9: Hone Your Description Skills

The goal of this exercise is to describe what you see inside and outside yourself.

- Sit in a public spot such as a café or park and describe one thing about each person that walks by.

- Pick up an object of beauty and describe it in as much detail as you can. Talk about its shape, size, color, and texture.

- Describe what someone has said to you in their exact words. Check and see to what extent you captured what they said.

- Describe a person's face as accurately as possible when they are happy, sad, excited, angry, and similar. Notice the shape and movement of different parts of their face and whether their skin changes color in accordance with their emotional state.

- Describe why you love your favorite movie or book so much. Try to identify at least three profound reasons why it made such a significant impact on you.

- Describe how the things someone says or does make you feel. For instance, "When you arrive late, I feel undervalued, and my thoughts are that I am stupid to always show up on time and hope you will do the same."

- Describe as many thoughts that pop into your head when you are feeling a strong emotion.

Hone Your Participation Skills

This exercise aims to help you connect more powerfully with the universe and with the moments you are living.

▶ EXERCISE 10: Hone Your Participation Skills

This exercise aims to help you connect more powerfully with the universe and with the moments you are living.

- Try to feel as connected as possible to the world around you. For instance, if you are lying in bed and a blanket is covering you, try to think of all the ways you are connected to that blanket. Think about what it is doing for you (for instance, keeping you warm or covering you), and think about its "kindness" in doing this for you. Touch the object and focus on the kindness it is exuding. Feel that you are deeply connected to that object and enjoy the sense of being loved.

- Put on your favourite dance tune and let your body move to the rhythm.

- Sing when you're having a shower or bath.

- Work out, focusing only on your exercises.

- Say a word repeatedly until you "become it." Positive words to repeat include "peace," "love," and "courage."

- Try an activity you haven't done before—acting, singing along to a karaoke machine, or taking up an outdoor sport like water skiing, snowboarding, or trekking.

EXERCISE 11: Conduct a Mental Body Scan

This exercise is ideal after a busy day at school or over the weekend. It provides stress relief, relaxes your muscles, and helps you reconnect with your body so you can listen to its wants and needs. After the exercise, you will feel calmer and more connected to yourself. This exercise is divided into three parts based on the different parts of your body: the lower body, upper body, and head.

Exercise 11 cont...

Boost your awareness of your lower body.

Sit or lie down somewhere comfortable and pay attention to the sensations in your lower body. Start with your toes and your feet. Is there any tension or pain in these areas? Are they tired from walking, running, or playing sports? As you focus on this part of your body, you may find that your mind wanders to events earlier that day or to worries. Accept these wandering thoughts as normal and gently take your mind back to your feet. If you feel tense in this area, breathe in and let go of the tension as you breathe out.

Do the same for the rest of your lower body—first your calves, then your knees, thighs, buttocks, and pelvic area. Remember to "breathe the tension out" of these areas if you feel tightness or tension. Take about five minutes for the first step.

Boost your upper body awareness.

Complete the same exercise as you did for your lower body, this time working on your upper body. Start with your torso and stomach, watching for sensations like tension, hunger, and any other sensations you notice. Next, move your attention to your lower back, chest (front and back), upper back, fingers, hands, forearms, elbows, and upper arms. Use your breathing to breathe out any tension or tightness. Spend another five minutes on this exercise.

Boost your awareness on your shoulder and head.

STEP 3

Your shoulders and head tend to accumulate stress and tension when times are tough. Try to notice this tension, tightness, or pain in these areas, beginning with the shoulders, then moving to the neck muscles, and then your head and face—including your forehead, eyes, nose, mouth, chin, and ears. Spend around five minutes on this area.

Use your journal to note down the sensations you felt in each area. You may find that you frequently have tension, pain, or tiredness in one or two areas. This is a good sign that you can benefit from working on relaxing these areas. For instance, if you have tension in your neck and shoulders, you can benefit from a few stretching exercises that soothe tightness.

EXERCISE 12: Counting Breaths

This exercise enables you to relax through breathwork. Before starting, observe how you are feeling. Are you stressed? Are you angry or in pain because of something that happened? Are you worried about an upcoming test? Once you are aware of how you feel, you can start.

Set your timer for ten minutes. Breathe in, and count from one to five on the exhalation. Count out loud or silently/in your mind, saying "One...two...three...four...five." Afterward, observe how you feel. Are you more relaxed now? Are you still worried? Use your journal to write down what this breathing exercise felt like.

EXERCISE 13: Thought Defusion Exercise—Writing Words in the Sand

Thought Defusion is a term taken from acceptance commitment therapy (ACT). It is very helpful in separating you from your thoughts—something that can be very useful when negative thoughts and intense emotions are threatening to take over your state of mind. Below is an exercise you may like to try out when it feels like it's all too much for you to handle.

Set your time for 10 minutes and close your eyes. Imagine lying on a beautiful beach with a large shore full of soft, powdery sand. As you calm down, try to become aware of your thoughts. What thoughts are most prevalent in your head today? Are they neutral or negative? Next, try to imagine that these thoughts are written on the sand. Watch the wind gently blow them away, or see the waves erasing them. As each thought goes, you begin to feel calmer and realize that thoughts are merely products of the mind. They are not you, nor do they have power over you.

Writing Words in the Sand

"Thought diffusion, rooted in Acceptance Commitment Therapy (ACT), aids in distancing from intrusive thoughts and overwhelming emotions. Explore this exercise to regain control when negativity overwhelms."

Instruction:

"Close your eyes for 10 minutes, picture a peaceful beach with soft sand. Think about today's thoughts. Imagine them on the sand, then let the wind or waves wash them away. Feel calm, knowing thoughts can't control you."

"Visualize this box as sand, and record what you wish to be washed away by the waves."

EXERCISE 14: Loving Kindness

In this exercise, you focus on sending good thoughts and energy to yourself and others. This is a nice way to start or end the day so you feel at peace with yourself when your head hits the pillow. Loving-kindness can be difficult to practice at first, especially when it involves someone you may be angry with. However, in time, you will find that it is immensely empowering.

1. Select someone you would like to send loving kindness to. It could be a friend, family member, or even yourself!

2. Sit or lie down with an "open stance" so you feel more relaxed. This means having your arms uncrossed and your palms facing up, resting gently on your legs as you sit or by the side of your body if you are lying down.

3. Start by breathing slowly and profoundly, and recite these wishes: "May I be happy, may I be healthy, may I be filled with peace." You can change these wishes to words that are more personal to you. If your thoughts wander, bring them back to these words. Continue saying them until you feel wrapped in love.

4. Work your way through the important people in your life, as well as those you may be angry at or in conflict with. Extend the words to them, as in: "May Judd be happy. May Judd be Healthy. May Judd be filled with peace."

III: Complete the HOW SKILLS Challenge

The WHAT skills challenge has taught you what to do when you are being mindful: observe, describe, and participate. HOW skills, meanwhile, tell you how to practice mindfulness. The three

HOW skills highlight how mindfulness should be practiced: non-judgmentally, one-mindedly, and effectively (Self Help Toons, n.d.).

EXERCISE 15: Non-judgementally

It is sometimes hard to catch yourself being judgmental. Here's an example of how you may often judge yourself without realizing it:

You observe that you are feeling angry, then you describe it to yourself. For instance: "My heart rate is rising, and I can feel my neck and ears going red." Now, here comes the judgment:

"I am wrong to feel angry because anger is a negative emotion."

Try switching it up and viewing anger non-judgmentally. Tell yourself, "Anger is an emotion that is neither good nor bad. Feeling angry does not make me bad. It is okay to feel this."

Exercise: The next time you are carrying out an everyday task, try to notice when you are making a judgment about yourself. Don't feel bad about doing so; just notice it and let the judgment go!

EXERCISE 16: One-Mindedly

This skill involves keeping your mind "in the here and now" instead of stuck in the past or present. This task requires a lot of practice, but you can do it! If you notice that there are a myriad of distracting thoughts stopping you from concentrating on a present task, try letting them go, just as you might let go of a negative thought or "ride through" a painful emotion. If you find that you are multitasking or doing several things at once, choose just one you want to do.

Exercise: Take your journal and write down the activities that make it easiest to feel mindful. These might include playing music, reading, or playing a computer game. Next, aim to focus your attention by boosting your present awareness. You can do this by (DBTSelfHelp.com, n.d.):

1. Focus your attention on the ground as you walk. Feel how it supports you and allows you to remain on your path.

2. Lie down in your bed and notice how the sheets feel on your skin. Notice how they embrace you and keep you warm.

3. Look at the four walls that surround you. Notice how they are connected with you through the floor and air. Feel how they guard and protect you so that you can get things done!

EXERCISE 17: Effectively

Doing things effectively simply means doing what works rather than what is "right" or "wrong." Being effective means freeing you of the burden of always having to be "right." For instance, if you are walking in the hallway at school and someone says something mean to you, you might consider it "fair" to answer them back with a similar statement. But how effective would this be at keeping you calm and enabling you to achieve your goals? Being effective is all about saving your energy for the things that matter and choosing the things that are worth fighting for (DBTSelfHelp.com, n.d.).

Exercise: Take your journal and write down one grudge you have against someone. Write down whether this grudge is benefiting you. Consider what an effective solution might be.

CONGRATULATIONS!

You have trekked through the
Mindfulness Section (Section 1) and
achieved the Ruby of Protection! If you
have the paperback edition of this
book, color the gem in and cut it out.
Put it on a poster or keep it in your
wallet as a reminder of the superpower
you have just discovered: mindfulness!
An award awaits you, in the form of a
Certificate of your ruby as a powerful
reminder of giving yourself fully to the
spectacular "here and now!"

Scan to receive

CELEBRATORY ACTIVITY:

A Mindfulness Meditation Session with your Ruby in

Son Doong Cave

Receiving the **Ruby** of Protection

Welcome to this DBT mindfulness script, which takes place within the coolness of Son Doong Cave—where the elusive Ruby of Protection is kept. In this transformative experience, you will immerse yourself in the depths of your emotions and tap into your Wise Mind.

Sit or lie down in a comfortable spot, close your eyes, and take a deep breath. Inhale to the count of five, then exhale to the count of seven. Visualize yourself standing at the entrance of Son Doong Cave, ready to embark on a journey to your inner world.

Step into the cave and notice the shift in the surrounding environment. Embrace the darkness as a metaphor for the mystery of your emotional landscape. Recognize that within this darkness lies the potential for growth and transformation. Feel a sense of protection from the cool cave walls, which keep you safe as you explore your emotions.

Turn your attention inward and gently explore the emotions that lie within you. Simply observe them without any judgment. Notice your sensations, emotions, and thoughts without pushing them away.

Become an impartial observer of your inner experience. Respond to these emotions with kindness and acceptance since they do not define you. Breathe deeply, allowing each breath to fill your heart with compassion and understanding.

Embrace the uncertainty and discomfort that may arise when negative thoughts and emotions reveal themselves to you, knowing that they are part of the journey towards protection and inner strength.

In the midst of darkness, a flicker of light calls your attention. It is the ruby. As you view it, embrace your own vulnerability and acknowledge the courage it takes to confront and embrace painful emotions. Recognize that being vulnerable enhances your strength and brings you closer to the Ruby of Protection.

The glimmer is arising from the rocks at the base of a large stalagmite in this cave called the Hand of the Dog. As you make your way to the stalagmite, you validate your experiences and exercise self-compassion and understanding. You know that by embracing and acknowledging painful emotions, you are transforming into the most powerful protector of your own emotions. You see the ruby and place your hands over it, feeling its texture and coolness. You feel a powerful protective energy arise within. You are filled with light and energy and spend a few moments enjoying this unique sensation.

Finally, you are ready to leave the cave. You leave the ruby where it is but carry its power of protection with you. Anytime you want to remind yourself of the value of acceptance and mindfulness, you can return to this cave.

As we conclude this DBT mindfulness script, remember that the journey into the depths of Son Doong Cave represents the brave exploration of emotions within yourself. Carry the essence of the Ruby of Protection into your daily life. May you find peace, healing, and growth as you continue to keep your mind in the present and accept your emotions as they are on your journey of self-discovery.

SECTION 2

CHAPTER 4

Take Charge of Your Emotions

GEM: The Sapphire of Emotion in Coron, Palawan

"Change your behavior, and you will change your emotions."

MARSHA M. LINEHAN

Your goal in Section 2 (Chapters 4 and 5) will be to find the Sapphire of Emotion by managing your emotions instead of allowing them to control you. In this chapter, you will discover what "emotional regulation" is. Next, in Chapter 5, you will get straight to work, completing a series of exercises and worksheets—so you can be the captain of your own ship of

The Sapphire of Emotion

The Sapphire represents intelligence and the ability to make good, wise choices. This sparkly blue gemstone was seen as a symbol of intelligence even back in ancient times. For instance, the ancient Greeks wore it to attain wisdom, and in ancient Persia, it was thought to strengthen your heart and give you courage. The Sapphire is a particularly powerful gem that symbolizes the world of emotions because your emotions are not more powerful than you are. Rather, by embracing skills that help you deal with tough emotions like anger, sadness, or disappointment, you can solve problems instead of allowing them to bring you down and keep you stuck in a rut.

Where is the Sapphire? Diving into a Hidden Lagoon in Coron, Palawan

In order to find this priceless gem, you will be mentally immersing yourself into a paradisiacal lagoon in Coron, Palawan—a beautiful island destination in the Philippines, in Southeast Asia. In order to reach the hidden lagoon,

The Sapphire of Emotion

The Sapphire represents intelligence and the ability to make good, wise choices. This sparkly blue gemstone was seen as a symbol of intelligence even back in ancient times.

The Sapphire is a particularly powerful gem that symbolizes the world of emotions because your emotions are not more powerful than you are.

Where is the Sapphire? Cont...

you will take a wooden boat to the entry point. The tide is high, so you must swim beneath a narrow cliff to get to the other side. When you emerge from the water, you are in a turquoise-blue lagoon surrounded by towering cliffs. You are all alone, and it feels wonderful to have all this beauty to yourself. Right next to the rock formation you swam under is a cliffside crevice. You swim up to it and see something flickering. It is the Sapphire of Emotion.

What is Emotional Regulation?

Earlier in Chapter One, we spoke of emotional regulation, or the ability to control or manage your emotions. The opposite of emotional regulation is emotional dysregulation—which is what happens when your emotions take over you. These terms are more complex than they sound. Essentially, they refer to the extent to which you are able to take the reins of your own emotions.

For instance, if you are given a bad piece of news—say you didn't do as well in your exams as you had hoped, Does it cause you to spiral into self-doubt and sadness or cause anxiety about your future? Or do you try to learn from your mistakes and formulate a strategy so you can improve your results the next time?

The first approach is "reactive." You react emotionally to the disappointment and get caught up in a hurricane of negativity. Sometimes, it can be so bad that you become stuck or frozen, and you just don't know what step to take next. The second approach shows emotional regulation. You are disappointed, and you acknowledge that, but you soon put your energy toward something positive: figuring out how to solve the problem.

The Hidden Lagoon in Coron, Palawan

"In order to find this priceless gem, you will be mentally immersing yourself into a paradisiacal lagoon in Coron, Palawan—a beautiful island destination in the Philippines, in Southeast Asia. In order to reach the hidden lagoon, you will take a wooden boat to the entry point. The tide is high, so you must swim beneath a narrow cliff to get to the other side. When you emerge from the water, you are in a turquoise-blue lagoon surrounded by towering cliffs. You are all alone, and it feels wonderful to have all this beauty to yourself. Right next to the rock formation you swam under is a cliffside crevice. You swim up to it and see something flickering. It is the Sapphire of Emotion"

The Process Model of Emotional Regulation

Emotional regulation has four "steps" or processes:

1 Situation:

A given event usually gives rise to specific emotions. For instance, a friend makes a mean comment, or someone gathers a group together and leaves you out.

2 Attention:

The situation commands your awareness, and you become aware of what has just happened.

3 Appraisal:

You perform an assessment of the situation. For instance, you conclude that their behavior is unjust or mean.

4 Response:

You have a physical and an emotional response to what has occurred. For instance, your heart may start beating faster, and you may feel pain in your chest. Your ears may get red and feel hot, and you may feel a ball of worry form suddenly in your tummy. Your emotional response may be hurt feelings, frustration, or anger. These responses lead you to react, and a new situation arises. The chain commences once again.

The Process Model of Emotional Regulation

Emotional regulation skills help you influence or change any part of this four-part sequence. For instance:

1. **Situation:** You can avoid situations in which someone is mean to you. For instance, if a classmate is consistently mean and puts you down, you can avoid spending time with them and invest more energy in people who care for you and make you feel good about yourself.

2. **Attention:** You can shift your attention to something else so your mind isn't centered on a hurtful or silly comment.

3. **Appraisal:** You can think about things differently. For instance, if someone says something sarcastic, you may conclude they are just having a bad day. This is especially true if the person is usually kind and accountable for their actions and apologizes for what they have said or done.

4. **Response:** You choose how you respond. For instance, if you would normally get into an argument with someone who said something nasty, you can walk away instead of engaging them.

Examples of Emotional Regulation Goals

Let's take a look at five emotional regulation goals:

1. You know that disappointments or put-downs happen frequently at school. You won't be able to avoid them all, but your goal is to stop them from bringing you down for the rest of the day (or the whole weekend). You want to minimize their impact on you and move onto a more positive emotion more quickly than you

have in the past.

2. Someone you know and cannot avoid puts you down frequently. This makes you feel small, upset, and sad because you are always kind to them. You want to stop what they say from making you feel bad about yourself.

3. You want to manage your emotions better so you can achieve another goal. For instance, if people frequently disrupt your classroom or speak loudly, you want to remain calm, so your teacher rewards your good behavior.

4. You may want to start taking better care of your emotions. For instance, if Twitter or Instagram are bringing you down (owing to discriminatory or angry comments or self-comparison), you may give yourself a social media break. When you do, you notice how pleasant it can be not to have to deal with the negative thoughts and emotions associated with constantly checking out your or others' channels.

5. You want to have more control over the intensity, duration, or type of emotion. For instance, you may want to hone your ability to think about something else when an emotion is trying to overtake your happiness and peace.

Three DBT Skills for Emotional Regulation

DBT can help you hone three skills that will empower you to deal with even the most intense and painful or distressing emotions. They are: understanding and labelling your emotions, reducing your emotional vulnerability, and decreasing your emotional suffering. We will go through each of these skills before moving on to the next chapter when you will complete a series of exercises to ace the Sapphire of Emotion challenge!

Understanding and labelling your emotions

When a distressing situation arises, it is normal to feel bad. However, the first step involved in emotional regulation is knowing how to identify the specific emotion you are feeling. As such, you can learn to tell yourself, "I'm feeling frustrated," "I'm feeling angry," or "I'm feeling disappointed," instead of just "I'm feeling bad."

It can also help to label the intensity of your emotions. To do so, check out this Wheel of Emotions, created by the renowned psychologist Robert Plutchik. The wheel shows that there are 8 basic emotions: joy, trust, fear, surprise, sadness, anticipation, anger, and disgust. However, each of these emotions has more and less intense versions. Pause for a moment and take a look at the wheel. Try to think of situations that may provoke the different emotions.

For example, If I am on my computer and my little sibling comes up and slaps their hand on the keyboard, and I lose the page I am on, I might feel annoyed. This emotion can be considered a mild form of anger. However, if I see someone be cruel to someone else, I might feel the powerful emotion of rage. A good way to track your emotions is to journal how key situations throughout your day made you feel. The more you get into the habit of writing down your feelings, the easier it will be to find the right words to express them.

The Wheel of Emotions

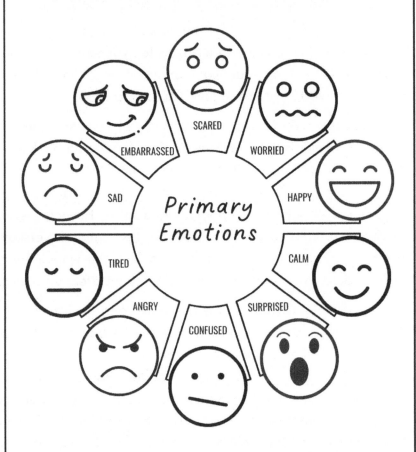

An emotion wheel, centered around basic or primary emotions, categorizes feelings like happiness, sadness, fear, anger, and disgust within a circular chart, aiding in emotional recognition and understanding.

Distinguishing Between Primary and Secondary Emotions

In order to manage your emotions, it also helps to distinguish between primary and secondary emotions.

Primary emotions involve initial reactions to events or environmental triggers. It is instinctive and natural and has an evolutionary function. For instance, when you win an important game at a sporting match, your primary emotion may be elation. On the other hand, you may feel instantly sad if you receive bad news.

Secondary emotions are those that are felt after the primary emotion has been experienced. They are learned or habitual responses. For example, after feeling sad about something, you may experience the secondary emotion of anger afterward. After feeling joy, you may feel pride later.

Secondary emotions often play an interesting role: that of covering up the sensitive part of emotions with something less sensitive. They protect you from feeling vulnerable.

Sometimes, however, secondary emotions can harm you in the long run. This is often true for emotions such as guilt, shame, frustration, and resentment. They are learned in childhood from parents or other significant people in our lives.

When trying to name your emotions, you will probably find that secondary emotions are harder to name. This is because they saturate the primary emotions with complex nuances. Secondary emotions influence your behavior. They are capable of intensifying your reactions. They also last far longer than primary emotions (Evans 2023). The good news is that they are also easier to control than primary emotions.

Primary and Secondary Emotions

Primary emotions are fundamental responses to specific situations, while secondary emotions are more complex, stemming from the interplay of primary emotions, thoughts, and external factors.

Primary emotions (Evans 2023):

- are instinctive and natural
- can feel painful or good
- can be harmful when you react to them
- are sensitive and vulnerable
- reside deep in your brain
- can help connect you to others
- can help guide your actions

Secondary emotions (Evans 2023):

- are learned or habitual
- are protective
- are defensive and avoidant
- can be controlled more easily than primary emotions
- can numb your emotions

An Example of Primary and Secondary Emotions at Work:

You get home after a long day at school on exam preparation week, and your bedroom is a mess. Your little sibling has pulled items off the shelf, and now, your floor is full of clothes, gadgets, and toys. You scream and lash out, saying, "I told you five thousand times NOT to enter my room when I'm not here!" You then take their toys and hide them while they cry and ask for them back. Your parent enters the room and grounds you both.

In this case, your primary emotion might be that of feeling overwhelmed by your upcoming exams. Instead of sharing your primary emotion with your family, you let your secondary emotion take over, and you begin to shout and raise your voice. Doing so doesn't actually relieve your stress and feeling of being overburdened. In fact, it makes you feel worse because now you're not getting on with your sibling or your parents. Your primary emotional needs may have been:

- "I wanted to come home and de-stress in my room listening to music."
- "I need support from my parents so my siblings respect my boundaries."
- "I need help."

By not sharing your feelings and bottling them up instead, you get the opposite of what you actually need.

Reducing Your Emotional Vulnerability

Have you noticed that you tend to snap or feel more anxious or depressed when you haven't got a good night's sleep or you haven't worked out in a while? The second DBT emotional regulation goal involves boosting your resistance to stress by embracing the skills contained in the acronym, PLEASE MASTER (Bray 2013).

PL	stands for taking care of your physical health and any illness or pain.
E	stands for eating a balanced diet and avoiding refined sugar, unhealthy fats, and stimulating foods and beverages containing caffeine.
A	is for avoiding alcohol and drugs, which only make emotional instability worse.
S	represents getting good quantity and good quality sleep.
E	means working out or getting enough exercise.
MASTER	refers to doing daily activities that make you more confident and boost your sense of competence.

To reduce your emotional vulnerability, try to take care of yourself and do things you love daily. The list of hobbies that fulfill you can be vast. It can include reading, swimming, playing an online game, spending time with a friend, or indeed anything you look forward to and enjoy. Simply taking part in the activities that fulfill you can reduce the risk of secondary emotions bringing you down.

Decreasing Your Emotional Suffering

When emotions like sadness, rage, or frustration arise, it can be tough to see the world in a positive light. The good news is that there are two skills you can harness to suffer less. They are:

Letting Go: Be aware of the emotion you are feeling, then let it go. You have already seen how you can achieve this through mindfulness practice. Acknowledging tough emotions instead of fighting, repressing, or avoiding them empowers you and helps you realize the extent to which you truly are the master of your own emotions.

Taking Opposite Action: Intense emotions can often lead you to take part in behaviors that make your situation worse—as seen in the example above of your sibling leaving your room in disarray. Sometimes, the most proactive, powerful action you can take is to do the exact opposite of what you normally do when you feel intense emotions.

You will learn how to apply your theoretical knowledge about emotional regulation to your everyday life in the next chapter as you make your way through various exercises that will help you find the Sapphire of Emotion.

CHAPTER 5

Complete the Emotional Regulation Challenge

PRIZE: The Sapphire of Emotion

"Just because you feel an emotion, that emotion does not mean you will act on it, nor does it define you. If you stuff it or bury it, the chances are good that it will resurface again at a later time when it is less convenient to deal with it."

MARSHA M. LINEHAN

If you sometimes find it hard to stop your emotions from getting the better of you, know that this is common, especially in the teen years. There are three main factors why you may find it harder to deal with tough emotions (Raising Children, n.d.):

1. Physical Factors: Your body undergoes many changes in your teen years, some of which may make you feel self-conscious and emotional. Another powerful reason is sleep. During your teen years, your body's internal clock is reset, and you start feeling sleepy later than usual. What's more, you are "programmed" to wake up later. Unfortunately, you usually have to get up early to make it to school on time, and that means that throughout the day, you can sometimes feel more tired and irritable (Nemours Teen Health, n.d.). That doesn't mean you have to just accept getting the poor quantity and quality sleep. However, you can do plenty to improve these areas of your life. To fall asleep deeply and profoundly, try to:

   - *Stop using screens at least an hour before you go to bed.*

   - *Stick to a regular sleep schedule and don't veer away from it.*

   - *Ensure your bedroom is cool (try to keep it at around 65ºF or around 17ºC), quiet, and dark. Ask your parents for blackout curtains if your room is close to a source of light, or use an eye mask, which is cheap but effective at blocking light out.*

   - *Avoid drinking coffee or consuming products with caffeine in the afternoon.*

In addition to getting good sleep, try to eat healthy foods (avoid refined and sugary foods) such as fruits, vegetables, and lean proteins, and make sure to exercise every day!

2. Brain Factors: In your teen years, your brain undergoes many changes. For instance, this is the time when your body is making sex hormones. These hormones cause physical, sexual, and emotional changes. Sometimes, this can lead to powerful emotions that can be confusing when you initially encounter them.

3. Social and Emotional Factors: You are moving toward independence, and right around this time, you may notice that you turn more to your friends than your family for approval. You are "living in your own head" more than you used to and thinking about social and other challenges.

For all these reasons, if things are feeling a bit jumbled up for you at the moment, know that you are definitely not alone. Even people who may always seem upbeat have to face all these changes … and you can do so with greater confidence, strength, and calm with DBT. Let's get right to emotional regulation so you can captain your own ship of emotions!

The Three Components of Emotional Regulation

You will recall from the previous chapter that there are three main components to emotional regulation:

I.   understanding and labelling your emotions

II.   reducing your emotional vulnerability

III.   decreasing emotional pain

There are 12 exercises in this section, each dedicated to one of these three components. Let's get to the first.

I: Understanding and Labelling Emotions: Challenge Yourself!

In Chapter 4, we mentioned the difference between primary and secondary emotions. You will recall that primary emotions are those that arise instinctively and quickly, while secondary emotions are your learned responses to these emotions. In the following exercises, we will focus on understanding and labelling both so you can take action to prevent you from engaging in harmful coping behaviors.

Exercise 1: Identify Your Feelings with the Emotion Wheel

When you're not feeling your best, it can be typical to say you feel bad or down in the dumps. However, naming your emotions with greater exactitude can provide emotional clarity and give you a deeper understanding of your triggers, how they affect you, and how to manage them efficiently. Naming your emotions also enables you to obtain a healthy distance from them to loosen their grip on you. Just by saying "I feel___," you bring your response to your emotions under your control, and you move on quickly instead of spiraling. By acknowledging your feelings, you become less reactive and enable yourself to be more assertive (Wilding, n.d.).

There are many ways to empower yourself to describe your emotions with precision. One of the most useful is Plutchik's Wheel of Emotions, which you encountered in Chapter 4.

Identify Your Feelings with the Emotion Wheel

This exercise is simple yet very rewarding. Simply take your journal and work on one or two basic emotions (and their more and less intense versions) and write down instances of when you felt these emotions.

For Example:

- **Anger:** I was angry when my best friend, Kai, canceled our concert outing. I had been looking forward to it all month and spent my allowance on the ticket.
- **Rage:** I felt rage when I saw a bully hit a younger child at recess.
- **Annoyance:** I feel annoyed when Tom starts talking in class or asking the teacher 1,000 questions and disrupting the class flow.

Your Turn:

Emotion	Situation

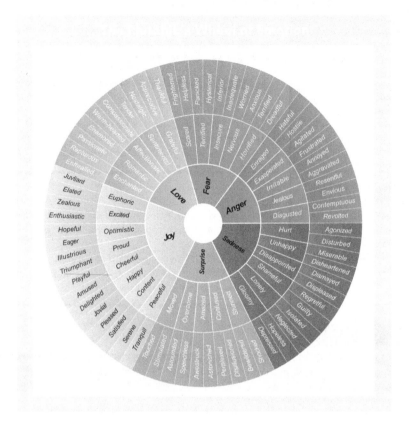

Exercise 2: Recognize Your Emotions

Marsha Linehan developed a six-step technique to help people see more clearly how their emotions can cause them to spiral out of control. When you become familiar with this technique, you can use it whenever you feel an emotional avalanche threatening to harm your peace of mind. By stepping aside and analyzing what is going on, you are well on your way to understanding that your emotions are not the boss of you. To perform this exercise for the first time, it pays to use your journal (Dialectical Behavior Therapy, n.d.).

STEP 1

Describe a situation in which you felt overwhelmed by emotions. Describe the situation—when and where it happened and what occurred.

For Example:

I was working on a group project with Sanam and Ella. We had to write about three states in the North of the U.S., and we each agreed to work on one state, supplying text and graphics for this part of the project. I worked hard on my part and stayed at home on Saturday afternoon to make sure it was done. I made sure to include all the information we agreed on—the climate, landscape, livelihood of the people, and places to visit.

Yesterday, when I uploaded my part to our joint Google Doc, I received a text from Sanam. She was angry because I had done too much work and "not left enough room for them." In fact, there was no limit, and they could write as much as they wanted. Neither of them had done any work, and the project was due in three days. What's more, I did not feel I had done anything wrong. I offered to cut down my part if they wanted, but she didn't answer. She eventually uploaded her part, but I noticed she had cut and pasted text from a page I had seen before.

STEP 2

What caused the situation?

I am not really sure what caused the problem. Perhaps we should have set a specific number of words and pages for each of us to complete.

STEP 3
What were your primary and secondary emotions?

My primary emotions were as follows: I felt instantly shocked and ashamed about having worked hard on my project. My secondary emotions then took over. I was scared to say anything about it, but I was angry that my attention had been called when it didn't seem she cared very much about the project at all.

STEP 4
Identify your urges.

My urge was to write her a text and say she was being unfair. What's more, she hadn't even started, so why was she so mad that I was actually working on the project?

STEP 5
What did you do?

I wrote her that I would be happy to cut down my part.

Outcomes.

STEP 6

I felt pretty good about the outcome. I cut down my part and did not criticize her text. I felt we were old enough to decide whether to write something original or copy. I was happy that things did not escalate, but I did suggest that next time, we should decide on a word count and page number so everyone knew how much or little to aim for.

Exercise 3: Setting Goals

When you're feeling low, being effective and getting things done (even if you have a small goal to fulfill) can help you get out of a rut and enhance the feeling that you are moving forward or getting somewhere. Sometimes, you won't feel particularly motivated to do so. This is a sign that it's the perfect time to do so! Sometimes, to change the way you think and feel about life, it pays to change one behavior. For instance, if you would normally just stay home and play on your computer, and you set a goal of meeting friends instead on a Saturday afternoon, you will most probably be really glad you took the decision to meet up. Think back on all the times you weren't too keen on doing something but did it anyway. Weren't you glad you didn't miss out?

This exercise has two parts. The first involves setting short-term goals, and the second involves long-term goals (Dialectical Behavior Therapy, n.d.).

PART 1

Setting Short-Term Goals

Think of three goals you can get done immediately or daily. Next, list the steps you will need to achieve these goals.

For Example:

Goal 1: I will practice mindful breathing for 10 minutes today.

Steps Involved: I will find an app with short exercises, find a quiet spot, and take part in the exercise.

Goal 2: I will eat 2 cups of fruit and 2.5 cups of vegetables.

Steps Involved: I will ask my parent or guardian to add these foods to the shopping list. I will pack one cup of fruit and vegetables for my school lunch and have the remaining portions when I get home.

Goal 3: I will do all my homework this afternoon.

Steps Involved: I will find a quiet study spot, leave all distractions (and my phone) in another room, and set

Setting Long-Term Goals

PART 2

Take time to set these goals, ensuring they are worth prioritizing. Try to think of things you've wanted to do for a long time but have somehow never pursued.

For Example:

Goal 1: I will work out 60 minutes a day, every day.

Steps Involved: I will start slowly, then work up my intensity. I will start with low-impact exercises and move on to higher ones. I will talk to my P.E. teacher and ask them if they can recommend a set of strength exercises I can do at home using my own body weight. I will look for useful online resources (such as videos) that can make my workouts more entertaining.

Goal 2: I will improve my report card this term.

Steps Involved: I will summarize my notes daily and do additional reading. A few weeks before the exams, I will start learning my notes and the additional information I have found. I will ask my teachers if there are any past exams I can use to practice my knowledge. I will stick to a sound sleeping schedule and exercise to reduce my stress levels. I will go to school on exam day feeling confident and try to see exams as a way to show my teacher how much I have learned. I won't cram and will walk into the exam room confidently.

Goal 3: I will expand my friendship group.

Steps Involved: I will chat with Maria and Phil every day. I will ask for their numbers and text them on Friday to suggest that we do something together on the weekend. I will sign up for scuba diving lessons in the summer so I can meet other people who love the sea. I will say "yes" when I am invited to a social occasion where I can meet new people.

Exercise 4: Being Aware of Cognitive Distortions

We all like to think we see the truth through a clear lens, but practically everyone has "filters" they use when emotions get high, and these filters distort what we perceive so that we see it as more negative than it actually is.

Before starting on this exercise, it pays to go through a few common cognitive distortions (Therapist Aid, n.d.).

1. **All-or-Nothing Thinking:** This bias leads you to see things as black or white, success or failure, good or bad. For instance, you worked hard to get an A on your English exam, but you got a B. When you use the all-or-nothing filter, you can tell yourself that "You're just no good at English" or that "You'll never get an A." In other words, this way of thinking can negatively affect your motivation and make you think of yourself as a

"loser" when you're not. Instead, it can help to take a calmer, evidence-based approach. Look at the exam and see the questions that your teacher marked down. Try to see what they wanted you to do and take note of it for next time. It can also help to talk to your teacher and ask them questions if you don't fully understand what they wanted from your answer. Ask them for more practice questions and ask your teacher to mark them for you so you know exactly what they are looking for.

2. **Overgeneralizing:** You know you are overgeneralizing when you use the words "always" or "never" a lot. For instance, if a friend is a little rude one day, and you say, "You always speak badly to me," this may not be true. They may usually be nice but lose their cool once in a while when they are tired or have faced disappointment.

3. **Using Mental Filters:** Using mental filters is the opposite of overgeneralization. Instead of taking one small event and overgeneralizing about it, you take one small event and focus on it so intently that it seems it is the only thing that matters. For instance, you give a presentation in your class and get an A. The teacher commends your work highly but suggests that you work on eye contact the next time. Instead of focusing on the whole event—the applause of your classmates or the teacher's smile and kind words—you focus on the one bad thing they said. You are giving a lot of importance to a tiny element in an otherwise positive experience.

4. **Jumping to Conclusions:** This distortion involves predicting that someone will act in a certain way or predicting an event will unfold in a certain way. For instance, you don't start eating fruits every day because you are sure you won't be able to stick to a healthy regimen.

5. **Emotional Reasoning:** When you use this distortion, you assume something is true just because you feel a certain way about it. For instance, if you feel guilty about saying no to someone, you conclude that you are a bad person. You can then engage in self-destructive behavior because you don't believe you are worthy of good treatment.

6. **"Should" and "Must" Statements:** Most of us use "should" or "must" several times a day, not realizing how constrictive these words can be. For instance, instead of saying, "I should lose weight," it is much more positive and motivating to say something like, "I am ready to commit to a healthier way of eating and getting fitter." When you tell yourself that you "should" be doing something, it can make you feel like a failure if you don't do it.

7. **Labelling:** Have you ever labeled someone with terms like "jerk," "bad person," or "selfish" because of one bad encounter? It pays to avoid labelling people, as it can distort our perception of who they are and lead to relationship problems.

8. **Personalization and Blame:** It is also human to blame ourselves or others for situations that are actually beyond our control. For instance, if you get a bad grade

These are just a few of the most common distortions people use on a daily basis. There are many more you can research if you're interested in psychology. Suffice it to say that these distortions can affect you deeply and lead you to a negative emotional state that can take a long time to get out of. They can also lead to behaviors that can be self-sabotaging and/or harm your relationships with others. These distortions are strongly related to automatic, negative thoughts (called ANTs). They are the thoughts that arise swiftly when a triggering situation presents itself. These thoughts can be so swift that you barely have time to realize that they are tainted by distortions (Hartney 2022).

The goal of this exercise is to help you stop cognitive distortions in their tracks so you can stay calm and take a solutions-based approach to any problem that occurs.

AUTOMATIC NEGATIVE THOUGHTS

The goal of this exercise is to help you stop cognitive distortions in their tracks so you can stay calm and take a solutions-based approach to any problem that occurs.

Examples:

DATE AND TIME	Tuesday, 12 pm
SITUATION	Ana didn't pick me for the science laboratory group work task.
AUTOMATIC NEGATIVE THOUGHTS	She's a terrible person. She always does this to me. She always excludes me.
EMOTION/S	I am devastated. I feel rejected, unliked, and angry. I would never do that to her.
YOUR RESPONSE	I tell her that I will never be in her group again.
A MORE ADAPTIVE RESPONSE	Get to know the other people in your group, and look forward to getting to know them better (since you usually work with Ana and your other friends).

DATE AND TIME	Friday, 5 pm
SITUATION	My aunt arrives and tells me I look beautiful but says that my dress would look nicer with different colored shoes.
AUTOMATIC NEGATIVE THOUGHTS	She's an old hag who's envious of me. She always puts me down. She looks for every single occasion to make fun of me and make me feel bad.
EMOTION/S	I am hurt and frustrated as I have to keep quiet so my mom doesn't get angry.
YOUR RESPONSE	I remain silent and try to avoid eye contact with my aunt.
A MORE ADAPTIVE RESPONSE	Thank her for her suggestion and even say I might try it next time, but that I think navy blue shoes look good with my cream-colored skirt.

AUTOMATIC NEGATIVE THOUGHTS

Experience 1:

DATE AND TIME	
SITUATION	
AUTOMATIC NEGATIVE THOUGHTS	
EMOTION/S	
YOUR RESPONSE	
A MORE ADAPTIVE RESPONSE	

Experience 2:

DATE AND TIME	
SITUATION	
AUTOMATIC NEGATIVE THOUGHTS	
EMOTION/S	
YOUR RESPONSE	
A MORE ADAPTIVE RESPONSE	

The above exercise is one of the most useful for reframing negative thoughts into more adaptive ones. Use this table regularly to examine how your automatic negative thoughts and filters can lead you to miss the mark and to analyze how an adaptive response can help you get over negativity rather quickly!

Exercise 5: Do the Opposite!

You know that emotional urges and automatic negative thoughts can act so quickly that they lead you to behaviors you can later regret. Opposite action is a DBT skill that involves choosing to do the exact opposite of what your emotions are telling you to do (Lorandini, n.d.). This is because you already know how emotions can take over and override the logical part of your brain.

Opposite action is not the same as repressing emotions. The key is to recognize your emotions, not judge them, and simply do the opposite so they do not drag you into behaviors with unwanted consequences.

Do the Opposite

Opposite action is not the same as repressing emotions. The key is to recognize your emotions, not judge them, and simply do the opposite so they do not drag you into behaviors with unwanted consequences.

For Example:

Situation	Emotion	Urge	Opposite Action
My boyfriend/ girlfriend broke up with me.	sadness, emptiness	I want to stay at home and listen to sad songs.	I will call my friend and go to see the latest Tom Cruise action film.
My classmate called me dumb.	Ashamed, angry.	I should keep quiet and stop contributing in class.	I will keep speaking my mind and doing research so I have excellent, evidence-backed points to make.
I have to give a presentation in front of class.	Extremely tense, almost crying.	I must tell the teacher I just can't do it.	I can walk out with a smile on my face and tell everyone that I'm nervous but that I am keen to share my research with them!

Opposite Action Activity

Your Turn:

Situation	Emotion	Urge	Opposite Action

Exercise 6: Exposure

We have mentioned that repressing or hiding your emotions can have a negative impact on your well-being. For instance, if you do all in your power to avoid situations that stress you out, then you may miss out on achieving your goals. If you try to avoid showing your emotions, then it may affect your ability to get close to others. Exposure therapy is what psychologists use to help people with strong fears and even phobias! If you are scared of dogs, then the only way to really get over your fear is to encounter them little by little (in measured, baby steps) until the fear dissipates.

For this exercise, follow these four steps (Dialectical

1. Identify an emotion you find hard to accept. For example, anger.

2. Observe the emotion. The next time you feel angry, notice how this emotion arises.

3. Expose yourself to your anger. Sit down, take a few breaths, and notice how intense your emotion is. Notice the bodily sensations that arise, and try to notice what stage the emotion is at. Is it just starting? Is it reaching its peak? Or is it simmering down? Allow yourself to feel this emotion with no judgment.

4. Sit with the emotion without acting on it. For instance, if you usually lash out at your sister when she does something that angers you, try avoiding the

and simply be with your emotions. Try to observe how you feel after a few minutes, one hour, and then a few hours.

Sitting with your emotions does not mean allowing others to step over your boundaries. Nor does it mean that you cannot express yourself. Instead, it involves dealing with a particularly intense moment and allowing yourself to just feel. Of course, when you feel calmer and have thought about the situation, asserting how you feel and asking to be treated well is beneficial.

Exercise 7: Following the Five-Step Problem-Solving Method

The next time you have a problem, try this powerful five-step method. Use your journal to describe how you completed each of the steps and the results they produced.

Step 1: Identify the problem.

Step 2: Brainstorm potential solutions.

Step 3: Weigh the pros and cons of each and choose one solution to try out.

Step 4: Try out the solution.

Step 5: Reflect on how it worked. If it didn't go as well as you wanted, try another solution and start again!

Exercise 8: Self-Validation

In DBT, self-validation is used to acknowledge, allow, and accept your emotions. Doing so is important because one of the reasons why emotions can be difficult to regulate is because you don't accept them.

Self-validation does not mean you must believe your thoughts or emotions are accurate. We have seen before how ANTs and cognitive distortions can sometimes skew the perspective. Self-validation is simply reminding yourself that it is okay to feel negative emotions and that you don't have to avoid or fear them.

Self-validation is also an excellent way to calm down when things are overwhelming. It involves a four-step process. Here is an example scenario with the steps in action:

1. **Observe:** I observe that my ears feel hot, my neck and shoulders tense up, and I have a fire in the pit of my stomach.

2. **Acknowledge:** Right now, I'm very angry.

3. **Allow:** This feels uncomfortable, but right now, it is how I feel. I am thinking negative thoughts about myself, but that does not mean they are true.

4. **Understand:** I am angry with myself because I allowed someone to walk all over my boundaries. I'm not going to judge myself for this because I wasn't in the mood to have a discussion. Instead, I'm going to do one thing to make me feel happier.

The Exercise:

1. *Describe a situation from the past when you experienced overwhelming thoughts and emotions.*

2. *How could you have responded to the situation using each of the four self-validation steps?*

3. *The next time you experience a difficult situation, practice these four steps and note how well this process worked for you.*

II: Reducing Your Emotional Vulnerability

When you are emotionally vulnerable, it means you have a strong, persistent emotional reaction to small events, and you can have difficulty modulating your facial expressions and behaviors. What's more, you may worry obsessively or find it difficult to stop going over painful situations repeatedly in your mind.

Emotional vulnerability can cause you to respond strongly and thereby cause hurt to yourself and others. It can interfere with your ability to think, plan, problem-solve, and consider others' perspectives. Additionally, it can make it harder for you to control your anger or frustration in emotionally charged moments. When emotions are intense, people sometimes try to escape them through behaviors that cause even more problems, such as drugs or alcohol.

DBT can help you feel more resilient and more in control of your emotions through mindfulness, emotional regulation, and "radical acceptance." We will delve into radical acceptance in Section 4, but in the meantime, we can keep working on emotional regulation.

Exercise 9: PL.E.A.S.E. MASTER Exercise

You will recall that in Chapter 4, I mentioned that the **P.L.E.A.S.E. MASTER** technique can help you grow your resilience in six fascinating ways. This exercise invites you to put the plan into action!

1 Name three things you will do today to care for your physical health or deal with any pain or illness you have. Example: I will brush, floss, use mouthwash, give my toes a manicure, and make an appointment to go to the dentist for a check-up and cleaning.

2 Name three things you will do to consume a balanced diet. Example: Today, I will eat green beans, watermelon, and an orange.

3 Write down your commitment to avoiding any substance that can make emotional instability worse. Example: I will avoid energy drinks containing a lot of caffeine, as that makes it harder to sleep at night," or "I commit to avoiding substances that can make me feel worse.

4 Write down three physical activities and sleep techniques you will use today.

Example: I will walk the dog for half an hour, meditate for 10 minutes, and stop using screens for two hours before going to bed.

5 Write down three exercises you will do. Example: I will do strength exercises for half an hour, go for a half-hour bicycle ride, and do a few stretches before and after my workout.

6 Write down three daily activities you will start embracing today that will build your confidence and make you feel competent. Example: I will write down a Haiku poem, revise my study notes, and sing for my siblings.

Exercise 10: Choose a Positive Activity

Choose from the following list of positive activities that can make you feel more grateful about the life you have. If none of them resonate with you, make up your own! Try to do at least two or three of these activities every day or as often as possible to give you a welcome buzz!

- [ ] soaking in a bubble bath or essential oil bath
- [ ] planning my next vacation with my parent or guardian
- [ ] listening to music
- [ ] remembering and writing down funny moments
- [ ] jogging or walking
- [ ] lighting a candle
- [ ] diffusing essential oils in my room
- [ ] wearing odd socks
- [ ] eating a meal you love
- [ ] buying something for your bedroom
- [ ] riding a bike
- [ ] bathing and drying my pooch
- [ ] collecting something (like shells, coins, or vintage clothing)
- [ ] camping outside
- [ ] training my dog or cat to do a trick
- [ ] dressing up
- [ ] doing yoga
- [ ] saying an affirmation before you head out the door in the morning
- [ ] doodling, drawing, or painting
- [ ] going for a swim
- [ ] planning a party
- [ ] hugging your sibling
- [ ] meditating
- [ ] going to the movies

III: Decreasing Your Emotional Pain

In Chapter 4, we mentioned that there are 2 DBT skills involved in lessening your emotional suffering. These are:

- letting go of the emotion through mindfulness

- taking opposite action

The following exercise will help you master these skills.

Exercise 11: Letting Go of Painful Emotions

It can be very hard to feel pain and move beyond it. It takes practice for everyone, even adults who seem to "have it all together." According to DBT theory, letting go of painful emotions involves the following steps:

1. **Observe your emotions.** You are a master at doing this now, thanks to your mindfulness practice, which you honed to collect the Ruby of Protection.

2. **Experience your emotions fully.** Don't reject it or try to make it less than it is, and don't make it bigger. It can be all too easy to obsess over a painful emotion like grief or sadness, making it strong enough to take hold of you.

3. **Remember that you are not your emotion.** Your emotion is part of you, but not all of you. Remember that everything passes and that you can feel very differently in a few days about something that is causing you great anguish today.

4. **Respect and love your emotions.** Love your emotions for what they are, even if they are tough and cause you pain.

Remember that there are no bad emotions—just emotions.

⇒ *Exercise: Use the above process for specific situations you encounter that cause you pain.*

⇒ *Examples: Your group partners hand in their work late, you lose a favorite device, a friend doesn't show up to a plan, or a sibling says or does something mean.*

⇒ *Feel free to think of the situations that are most pertinent to you!*

CONGRATULATIONS!

You have officially immersed yourself in the lagoon of your feelings and have achieved the Sapphire of Emotion! Put it on a poster or keep it in your wallet as a reminder of the superpower you have just discovered: that of managing your emotions!
You are set to receive a certificate of your Sapphire, serving as a potent reminder of your ability to tackle distressing emotions without letting them take over your identity or your peace of mind!

Scan to receive

CELEBRATORY ACTIVITY:

A Mindfulness Meditation Session with your Sapphire in Coron

Receiving the **Sapphire** of Emotion

Welcome to this mindfulness meditation session at the hidden lagoon in Coron, Palawan. Get ready to embark on a journey of emotional regulation and exploration, seeking the metaphorical Sapphire of Emotion within yourself. As we ride through the waves of emotion, you will find inner peace, understanding, and a deep connection with your emotions.

Sit or lie down in a comfortable spot, close your eyes, and take a deep breath. Inhale to the count of five, then exhale to the count of seven. Visualize yourself standing at the edge of the hidden lagoon, surrounded by the breathtaking beauty of nature. The tranquil waters mirror the vastness of your emotions, calm on the surface yet holding depths of unknown feelings. As you step into the lagoon, let the water symbolize the flow of your emotions.

Now, turn your attention inward. Begin to explore the currents of your emotions without judgment or resistance. Observe any sensations that arise within your body. Notice the thoughts and memories that may float to the surface of your mind. Allow any emotions that come up to be acknowledged and felt, just as the water of the lagoon allows ripples to form and fade.

With each breath, embrace your emotions with compassion and acceptance. Be kind to yourself, recognizing that emotions are a natural and essential part of your human experience. Allow yourself to fully feel them without trying to repress or change them.

If the emotions that arise make you feel uncomfortable, focus once again on your breathing. Feel the rhythmic pattern accompany you back to a state of serenity and mindfulness.

As you continue this inward journey, envision the metaphorical Sapphire of Emotion, gleaming within a crevice of the cliff at the entrance to the hidden lagoon. This precious gem represents emotional regulation and the ability to find balance amidst the ever-changing tides of feelings. Trust that you have the capacity to access this emotional equilibrium within yourself.

The Sapphire of Emotion radiates a serene blue light, illuminating your chosen path. Allow its calming energy to fill your being. As you hold this metaphorical gem in your hands, feel the sense of emotional clarity and stability it brings.

Remember, just like the lagoon, your emotions are fluid and changeable. Embrace the impermanence of your feelings, knowing that every wave will eventually recede. Through emotional regulation and mindfulness, you can navigate the waters of your inner world with an equal measure of strength and grace.

Before you leave the hidden lagoon, take a few seconds to express your gratefulness. Acknowledge the strength it takes to face tough emotions without letting them overwhelm you.

Carry the essence of the Sapphire of Emotion within your heart, knowing that you can access this inner gem whenever you need emotional support. As you open your eyes and return to your daily life, remember the wonderful sensation that arose when you realized that you are the ultimate captain of your emotions. Embrace them with compassion and allow the Sapphire of Emotion to guide you on your journey

Let Other Teens Know That There Is a Way to Manage and Overcome Tough Emotions

Radical acceptance rests on letting go of the illusion of control and a willingness to notice and accept things as they are right now, without judging

MARSHA M. LINEHAN

At the beginning of this book, I mentioned that Dr. Marsha M. Linehan developed DBT after a difficult youth—one involving stays in psychiatric institutions and various self-destructive events, most likely due to undiagnosed BPD. It is, perhaps, precisely because she had been through the same pain her patients were dealing with that she gained a profound understanding of emotional dysregulation and devised a system that worked.

Linehan's breakthrough arose when she realized that you might not be able to escape from pain or simply push it away, but if you "ride through it" as though it were a wave, you will realize that emotions—even very difficult ones—are not permanent. What's more, they do not define you.

For Linehan, the key to living a full life lay in accepting even the toughest emotions, followed by a commitment to take critical steps for a happier life.

By this stage of your reading, I hope you have already realized the powerful effect that your own Wise Mind can have on your life. I hope you are harnessing techniques such as taking the opposite action and relying on the PL.E.A.S.E MASTER strategy to boost your resilience to stress. Many people who are new to DBT are surprised by the fast-acting effects that these and other DBT strategies can have. And I hope that they are already making a vast

If this book is helping you see the powerful role you play in choosing how to respond to tough emotions, please leave me a review on Amazon.

Like Marsha Linehan, my life's quest is to help others realize that you can't evade all the curveballs that come your way. But you can minimize their impact through specific strategies that decrease emotional suffering.

By leaving a review and sharing a bit about your story, you can let other readers know they can be far more resilient than they ever thought possible. With the help of DBT, they can climb out of the pit of despair and achieve a meaningful and full life.

SECTION 3

CHAPTER 6

Why is Interpersonal Effectiveness so Important

GEM: The Tsavorite of Connection in Leopard Hill

"Love seeks no reward but when given freely comes back a hundredfold. "

MARSHA M. LINEHAN

Your aim in Section 3 (Chapters 6 and 7) will be to find the Tsavorite of Connection by harnessing the superpower of mindfulness or keeping your mind "in the present moment." In this chapter, you will discover how DBT can help you get on with others and hone your interpersonal skills. Next, in Chapter 7, you will get straight to work, completing a series of exercises and worksheets—so you can practice what you've learned with others.

The Tsavorite of Connection

When you think of bright green stones, you probably think of emeralds, but high-quality Tsavorite stones of more than two carats are rarer than emeralds. The Tsavorite was first discovered by the geologist Campbell R. Bridges in Tanzania in 1967, then in Kenya in 1970 (Tsavorite, n.d.). Bridges was a bit of a real-life Indiana Jones. He used to spend his nights in 30-foot-high treehouses to avoid elephants, cobras, scorpions, and other dangerous animals while he was on his quest for precious gems.

The Tsavorite of Connection

The Tsavorite is an expensive gemstone, owing to its scarcity. It is multiple times rarer than other precious gemstones and has greater transparency and brightness. Tsavorites are so rare in nature that stones bigger than five carats are extremely rare to find, and geologists believe that Tsavorite mines may soon go extinct.

These gemstones are believed to have metaphysical properties, including healing, protection, and luck. They are thought to improve the clarity of perception, knowledge about love, and understanding of other people—which is why it is the ideal stone to represent healthy, fruitful interpersonal relationships.

Where is the Tsavorite? Climbing up the Treehouse on Leopard Hill

Campbell R. Bridges built a treehouse in Leopard Hill (located around 190 miles southeast of Nairobi), and when he wasn't there, leopards used to visit his abode. They would leave the only thing that remained from the meals they

had a pet python called Patrick, who used to guard his treehouse to protect his precious gems when he was away (Davison 2009). Are you ready to befriend Patrick and get your hands on the sparkling green gem?

Why is Interpersonal Effectiveness a Superpower?

Interpersonal effectiveness is a skill that helps you get the most out of relationships and be respectful to yourself and others. If you want to build healthy relationships with others, it is important to do the following (Tara Arnold Inc, n.d.):

- Take care of the key relationships in your life. By attending to small stressors as they arise, you can keep important relationships intact.
- Balance needs and demands. While being a giving and kind person is important, neglecting your needs to fulfill others' demands is harmful.
- Balance your "wants" with your "shoulds." Everyone has responsibilities, but it is also vital to enjoy pleasurable moments and do the things you love.

Leopard Hill, Nairobi

Ready to befriend Patrick and discover the sparkling green gem?Interpersonal effectiveness is a superpower for nurturing relationships, and respecting yourself and others. To succeed, focus on key relationships, balance needs, and demands, prioritize wants alongside responsibilities, and build mastery and self-respect.

- Build mastery and self-respect. Building mastery involves doing things that make you feel competent. To exercise self-respect, you must be effective in asking for things and comfortable saying no when you don't want to do something or when something doesn't feel right.

Why is Interpersonal Effectiveness so Important?

The quality of your relationships affects your self-esteem, confidence, well-being, and sense of purpose. Interpersonal effectiveness helps you to do the following (Morgan 2021):

- Communicate well with others. Receive and provide information and utilize the right verbal and non-verbal tools to relay your message.
- Be empathetic with others. Put yourself in someone else's shoes, trying to understand why they think, feel, or behave the way they do.
- Be a great team leader. Leaders get things done, motivate others, and show innovation and courage. Leadership is a vital skill, not only now but also when you are an adult.
- Handle conflicts well. Conflicts or disagreements can arise throughout the day, even with people you know and love. All people have different wants and priorities, and when these clash, it can lead to conflicts. The good news is that conflicts also help you know each other better and

figure out ways to find solutions that take everyone's wishes into account.

- Work well as part of a team. At school, you have probably worked on group projects at various times. If so, you know that they can be challenging because you may disagree with how a task should be carried out or who should do what. Interpersonal effectiveness helps you weather these challenges well and minimize tension between team members.
- Have a positive attitude: When your relationships with people around you are optimal, it is easy to

Important Interpersonal Skills That Will Help Your Thrive

There are many interpersonal skills that are worth discovering and utilizing in your life. These include the following (Skills You Need, n.d.):.

Communication Skills. These skills help you communicate information accurately, clearly, and as intended. There are three types of communication:

- Verbal: what you say and the tone of voice you use
- Nonverbal: the way you relay your message with your face and body
- Listening: not just hearing what someone says, but being present for them and helping them feel heard

EMOTIONAL INTELLIGENCE

The ability to express and control your own emotions while also understanding others, interpreting their words and actions, and responding to them. Through emotional intelligence, you can do many things, including (Cherry 2023):

 IDENTIFY AND DESCRIBE WHAT PEOPLE ARE FEELING.

BE AWARE OF YOUR OWN STRONG POINTS AND LIMITATIONS.

 HAVE SELF-CONFIDENCE AND SELF-ACCEPTANCE.

KNOW HOW TO LET GO OF MISTAKES.

 BE WILLING TO ACCEPT AND EVEN LOOK FORWARD TO CHANGE.

BE INTERESTED IN OTHERS AND THE WORLD AROUND YOU.

 FEEL EMPATHY FOR THOSE WHO ARE HAVING A BAD TIME.

BE SENSITIVE TO OTHERS' WANTS AND NEEDS.

 OWN YOUR MISTAKES.

MANAGE YOUR EMOTIONS IN TENSE OR STRESSFUL MOMENTS.

Working Alongside Others: Working in a group involves taking account of others' wishes in addition to your own. Being a strong team player helps make you likable and makes others want to work with you.

Negotiating, Persuading, and Influencing Others: When you have a great idea or you have a plan or activity you'd like to invite others along to, being able to inspire them and influence them is a great skill to have. In order to influence others, they have to trust you. They know that if you propose it, it's likely a good idea to sign up for it!

Conflict Resolution and Mediation: Who said conflicts always had to be a bad thing? Quite the contrary! Disagreements are a magnificent opportunity to learn more about how others think and feel, as well as discover their wants and needs. They also help you uncover their conflict style. For instance, have you noticed how some people rush in to solve a disagreement quickly while others seek a bit of space? Resolving conflicts means knowing that all relationships are about give and take. They don't work well when one person does all the giving, and the other does all the taking.

Problem-Solving and Decision-Making: Problem-solving and decision-making involve the same essential process. When you have a big decision to make or an obstacle standing in your way, you can either get drowned by the weight of it or resolve to find a solution. As mentioned in Chapter 5, the process essentially involves identifying the decision or problem, thinking up a few positive solutions (weighing the pros and cons of each option), making your choice, and then reflecting on how it went. If it went well, then hooray! If it didn't, you can try another of the solutions you thought of.

Maintaining Your Integrity: Personal integrity can be defined as being honest and ethical and living according to your values and principles. For instance, if you are a strong advocate for environmental sustainability, then in order to maintain your personal integrity, you probably undertake several actions. You may recycle, take part in beach or park clean-ups, and reduce your carbon footprint by taking the bus instead of asking your parents to drive you somewhere.

Interpersonal Effectiveness and Boundary Setting

Having good relationships involves how you behave toward others and the steps you take to respect yourself and set healthy boundaries. Boundaries keep you safe. They let others know what is most important to you. They let people know what to expect if they want to get on with you. Boundaries are flexible. You may find that as the years go by, you decide to change them—and that is perfectly healthy. For instance, you may initially be fine with lending your car now, but later, when you start working and buy the car of your dreams, you may be more reluctant to lend it to others.

Seven Types of Boundaries to Protect

There are a myriad of boundaries you can set up. Some of the most common include (Martin 2020):

1. **Physical Boundaries:** These boundaries protect your space and body. For instance, you may not be comfortable when someone stands too close to you or when someone you don't know well gives you a hug.

Types of Boundaries to Protect

Establishing boundaries is vital for self-respect and healthy relationships, covering physical, sexual, emotional, mental, spiritual, financial, and time aspects. Non-negotiable boundaries prohibit abuse and maintain personal safety (Martin 2020).

Common Boundaries include (Martin 2020):

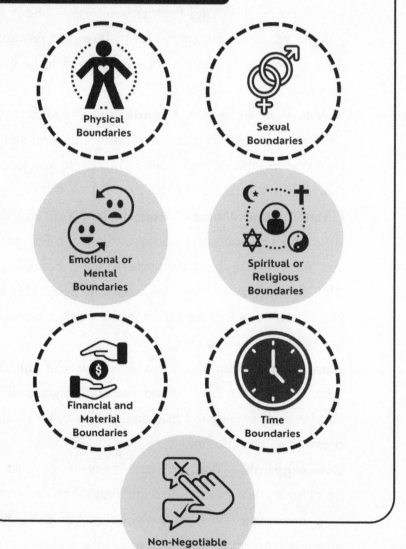

Physical Boundaries

Sexual Boundaries

Emotional or Mental Boundaries

Spiritual or Religious Boundaries

Financial and Material Boundaries

Time Boundaries

Non-Negotiable Boundaries

2. **Sexual Boundaries:** These protect your right to consent, define what type of touch or intimacy you are okay with, and your right to ask honest questions about your partner's sexual history. For instance, you may not want things to get "romantic" until you know someone well.

3. **Emotional or Mental Boundaries:** These safeguard your right to think and feel as you wish, without others judging you or ridiculing you for it. They also protect your right to have your feelings respected and to keep some things private to yourself.

4. **Spiritual or Religious Boundaries:** These boundaries protect your right to your own spiritual and religious beliefs and practices and your right not to be forced or urged to follow someone else's.

5. **Financial and Material Boundaries:** You can decide what you do with your money and things. For instance, you may not feel comfortable loaning someone over $50, or you may not lend anyone your books (for example, if you have loaned books in the past and they have not been returned to you).

6. **Time Boundaries:** These respect how you spend your time. It is okay to tell a friend you can only see them for two hours this weekend because you've other plans or a project to catch up on.

7. **Non-Negotiable Boundaries:** These are "must-have" boundaries that you need to stay safe. For instance, any type of abuse, physical violence, or drug or alcohol abuse is a no-no for you, and you make it clear.

How Can Setting Boundaries Help Improve Your Interpersonal Effectiveness?

Boundaries are helpful because they clarify things for yourself and others. Once friends and loved ones know your boundaries, they are usually keen to protect them and careful not to overstep them (Holmes 2016). Within healthy relationships, boundaries can:

- boost self-awareness
- help you be a better friend, family member, or partner
- empower you to exercise greater self-care
- reduce stress
- enhance your communication skills
- boost trust
- reduce anger
- help you harness the power of saying the word "No" and not apologizing for it
- empower you to do the things you actually want to
- make you and others more understanding

Finding Friends and Boosting Your Conversational Skills

When you have your interpersonal skills down pat, it's much easier to make friends while still retaining your sense of self. If you are new to town, you want to expand your friendship circle, or you simply want to connect with people with similar interests, then the following strategies can help:

1. **Sign up for a group activity.** Think of the one talent, skill, or sport you wish you knew or could play. Signing up for extracurricular classes is always more motivating

when the main focus is an interest or hobby. Whether it's Dungeons & Dragons, swimming, or capoeira, aim to find a group activity where you can meet and mingle with people your age.

2. **Be open to trying new things.** People who are willing to try new activities and do something they've never done before (from playing football to signing up for the school musical) are fun because they are so spontaneous. On the other hand, people who are rigid or inflexible (those who only want to stick to the things they already know, like, or excel at) can be harder to connect with.

3. **Hone your conversational skills.** Friendship always starts with a conversation and a meeting of minds. They say that conversation is an art; indeed, before starting or joining a conversation, it pays to be observant of verbal and non-verbal cues. For instance, if you see a small group talking and they look serious or create a kind of physical barrier by turning their backs to you, it's a good sign that perhaps they are talking about something private and that others are not welcome. On the other hand, if you walk by and see that people in a group are looking around and someone catches your gaze, go up and ask them what's up. Show interest by asking them to put you up to speed and asking open-ended questions starting with "Wh" words like What? Where? When? Why? Once in a while, nod or say phrases like "I get it," "Yes, of course," or "I feel you." Look them in the eye as they talk to show they have your attention—but make sure you're not staring! Be watchful of when they seem to want

to end a conversation. They may say, "Oh well then," "So…" or "Well…" or simply look away like they are finished talking about a subject. To end a conversation politely yourself, acknowledge their value and say you have to go. For instance, you might say, "I enjoyed our chat, but I have to go and study for the test tomorrow. See you tomorrow," or "Hey, my mom's arrived. I have to go; see you soon."

4. **Validate others.** Validating others simply means acknowledging another person's thoughts, feelings, experiences, values, and beliefs. It isn't about agreeing with everything they say or trying to fix them. It simply involves accepting them as they are and honoring their thoughts and opinions, even when they differ from your own.

5. **Be a good friend. Be honest, loyal, and trustworthy.** When a friend confides in you, keep what they say private, even if you argue and even if the friendship ends. When you do have disagreements, sort them directly with each other instead of talking to others. Gossip has a bad way of getting around, and you could regret something you said in the heat of the moment.

The Three Main DBT Goals for Interpersonal Effectiveness

DBT embraces three key goals to enhance your relationships with others:

1. *Objective Effectiveness:* This goal involves getting what you want. For instance:

⇒ *You stand up for your rights because you want to be taken seriously.*

⇒ *You ask someone to take you home if others at the party start drinking.*

⇒ *You say no to an unreasonable request, and you don't give in when someone tries to overstep your boundaries.*

2. ***Relationship Effectiveness:*** This goal is centered on maintaining and/or improving your relationship. For instance:

⇒ *You balance a short-term desire with something that's good for a long-term relationship.*

⇒ *You ask for something nicely, and the person feels motivated to do it for you.*

⇒ *You say no kindly, doing so in such a way that the other person's feelings are not hurt.*

3. ***Self-Respect Effectiveness:*** This skill involves asserting yourself, asking for something, or saying no. The aim with this one isn't so much to get what you want (as it is with objective effectiveness) but rather to maintain your morals, beliefs, and values (Hall 2021). For instance:

⇒ *You have a friend that others have purposely left out of a plan. You stand up for them and are willing not to go along if they segregate this person for no good reason.*

In many cases, one situation will challenge you to exercise all three goals. Let's see three examples in which this might be the case. In all the examples below, you are called upon to exercise relationship, objective, and self-respect effectiveness:

Example 1: You are working on a group project and need your team members to pull their weight. You value them and don't want to fight, but some are not doing any work and leaving it to the rest of the group.

Example 2: A classmate who spends a lot of time with you at school and whom you consider one of your best friends has a party and invites other people but does not invite you.

Example 3: You are at a friend's house when their older sibling approaches you and offers you a beer. Your friend grabs one, but you don't want to. You don't want them to think you are uncool, but you do not drink and are not willing to give in.

Factors Reducing Interpersonal Effectiveness

In the same way that some skills can make your interactions with others more effective, some factors can stand in the way of friendships and relationships. They include (DBTSelfHelp.com, n.d.):

- **A Lack of Skill:** People learn skills by observing others and practicing them in their daily lives. However, if you don't have anyone to model skills for you, you don't have the opportunity to observe vital skills, or you don't have the chance to practice them, then you can lack them. The good news is that it is never too late to learn, and DBT can help you make up for lost time.

- **Worry Thoughts:** It can be hard to take part in conversations, assert your wants, needs, and boundaries, and try new things out if you are worried about what others will think of you or if you worry about failure. Always remember that failure is a fantastic opportunity to grow and refine your strategies!

- **Emotions:** If you are very angry, frustrated, or anxious, your emotions can overwhelm you and shut you down. Remember the techniques you learned in the first section, and use mindfulness techniques and breathing to get to a calmer state. Always consult and pay heed to your Wise Mind. It really does know best!

- **Indecision:** Not knowing what decision to make can keep you stuck in a rut. This can occur when your priorities are in conflict, you don't know how to strike the perfect balance between asking for too much and too little, or you don't know how to balance saying no with giving in to everything. Rely on your Wise Mind to make a reasoned but intuitive decision, and consider the pros and cons of different choices before settling on one!

Now that you are aware of what interpersonal effectiveness is and why it is so important, let's get right to the activities that will strengthen relationships. As you complete them, you will be taking big steps toward the beautiful Tsavorite hiding in that wooden treehouse in Leopard Hill!

CHAPTER 7

Complete the Interpersonal Relationship Challenge

PRIZE: The Tsavorite of Connection

"If you are with someone who is in hell, keep loving them,

because in the end it will be transformative."

MARSHA M. LINEHAN

When you're at school, making friendships and connections almost seems like a given. You either "click" with people or you don't, and friendship groups can form quickly—sometimes at the expense of really getting to know others and seeing what you have in common with them.

Sticking only to the people you know well not only stops you from getting to really know others (and discovering awesome things about them) but can also contribute to disagreements and conflicts. It can also stop you from learning how to set boundaries with people you are not 100 percent comfortable with, yet doing so is vital for your well-being and happiness.

We mentioned previously that conflicts can be positive in many ways. For one, they enable you to get to know someone on a deeper level. That person may surprise you positively by being kind and understanding despite the fact they are having a disagreement with you. Conflicts are also an excellent opportunity for you to say what you want and need assertively and clearly, without losing your cool and without saying "Yes" all the time, just to appease others.

In Chapter 6, we mentioned that there are three main DBT goals for interpersonal effectiveness:

- Objective Effectiveness—or getting what you want

- Relationship Effectiveness—or maintaining and improving your relationships

- Self-Respect Effectiveness—making sure you don't disrespect yourself just to make everyone else happy

The challenges in this chapter will be divided into these three categories so you can master the skills you need to build healthy relationships and a strong sense of self-respect. Let's get cracking!

I: Objective Effectiveness

Exercise 1: DEARMAN

DEAR MAN is a strategy that enables you to say how you feel and express your wants and needs assertively.

The acronym DEAR MAN stands for:

D	**D**escribe the current situation
E	**E**xpress your feelings
A	**A**ssert yourself
R	**R**einforce
M	stay **M**indful
A	**A**ppear confident
N	**N**egotiate

What Are Your Goals?

In order to carry out the DEAR MAN steps (Therapist Aid, n.d.), you need to first know what your goals are. When you are in the process of defining them, aim to:

1. Prioritize high-priority demands if you have little time.

2. Balance your "wants" against your "shoulds." Consider if you are agreeing to do something because you "should" do it. Aim to do what you authentically want to do.

3. Ask for support if you need it.

This exercise can be carried out when you want to express yourself with someone else. The next time you have something you want or need from someone else:

1. Describe the situation. Write down only the facts. Avoid making judgments about who caused the situation and whether it is good or bad.

   Example: "We agreed to go snowboarding today, and you ended up going skiing with Sarah."

2. Express how you feel about the situation, using "I" statements, so the other person doesn't feel like you are blaming them.

   "I felt like I wasn't very important to you because I had been really looking forward to our plan."

3. Assert yourself by asking what you want or need. Be clear and direct so the other person understands you completely and there is no room for misunderstanding.

   "The next time we make a plan, I'd like you to honor it as much as possible."

4. Reinforce the plan. Let them know that there will be a

positive outcome if they comply with your request or a negative outcome if they do not respect what you have asked for.

> "If you don't do this again, I won't take it into account. However, if we already have a firm plan and I prepare for it and you cancel at the last minute, I will have to stop making plans to meet you."

5. Be mindful. Keep your eye on your goal, repeat what you have said if necessary, and don't get pulled into mud-slinging or blaming.

6. Appear confident, employing an assertive tone and body language.

7. Negotiate. Be confident but also flexible. Offer alternative solutions so you can achieve what you want. For instance, you might suggest,

> "Next time, we can ask Sarah to join us."

Think of the last time you had a conflict or a situation you weren't happy about with a friend. Take your journal and write down a script of what you would tell them using the DEAR MAN method.

II: Relationship Effectiveness

Exercise 2: GIVE

This technique helps you keep things calm during a discussion or argument. Try it out when you're not in an argument (during a typical conversation) so you get used to it. This technique takes practice, but if you embrace it consistently, you will achieve so much and enrich your relationships greatly!

GIVE stands for:

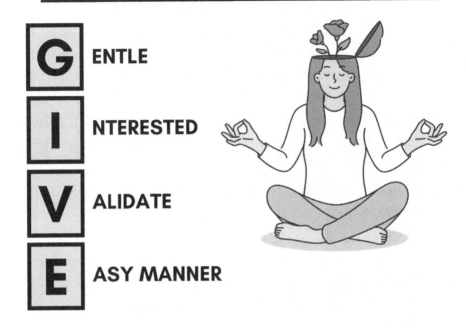

G ENTLE

I NTERESTED

V ALIDATE

E ASY MANNER

Once again, it is crucial to know what you want to achieve before you speak with the other person. Goals may include doing the following:

- Let them know their wants and needs matter to you.

- Act in a way that won't make them feel defensive. By doing so, you will have a better chance of getting what you want. Remember that people tend to shut down or put up a defensive wall when they feel attacked.

- Balance your short-term goals with what is good for your relationship in the long term.

Write down:

- 3 phrases you can say to show you are interested in what they have to say. For instance: "I would love to hear your opinion on this."

- 3 phrases that validate what they are saying. For instance: "Yes, of course, I would feel that way too. I get

- 3 ways you can make the conversation easier. Hints: humor, being friendly, and being easy-going. For instance: You can nod, make a joke about something you both find funny, or smile when they say something humorous or ironic.

Exercise 3: Validating

Validating in DBT involves finding the kernel of truth in someone else's perspective. It does not mean you have to agree with or approve of what they are saying or doing. Your aim is simply to understand where they are coming from.

Marsha Linehan defines validation as communicating to someone that their responses make sense and are understandable within their current situation. Try to think of it as a refusal to treat someone like they are bad, crazy, or wrong, even when their behavior is difficult to validate. Remember: You can disagree with someone AND validate them at the same time (Vaughn, n.d.).

The Six Levels of Validation

There are six levels of validation in DBT. The highest is called "radical genuineness." The six levels are (Creative Healing Philly 2021):

1. Show interest and show the person you want to listen to them. This sounds easier than it can be in real life. When you are in an argument with someone, it can be hard to refrain from rolling your eyes or rushing to blurt out your point of view. However, if you can do it, you are already on the road to a peaceful solution based on true understanding.

   Example: Look the person in the eye, stay present, and don't check your phone while they are speaking.

2. Accurately reflect on what they have said. This involves asking questions to clarify what the person has said and letting them know you are listening to them.

   Example: Your friend Penelope tells you that she

doesn't like it when you bring up embarrassing stories from the past when you are with people you don't know well.

You can reflect on what they have said by saying, "Okay, so I hear you saying that you don't want me to bring up stories about us from the past when we are with people we aren't very close to." She says, "Yes," and you say, "Is there more you would like me to do?"

3. Put yourself in their shoes. Imagine how that person feels.

Example: You can imagine that she is a little more introverted than you and feels uncomfortable when people she doesn't know well laugh at her. This might be the case, even if their intention is to laugh with her.

4. Validate what they are saying based on history. Example: "Yes, I know you generally don't like revealing too much about yourself when you don't know someone well."

5. Recognize that their emotional reaction is one anyone would have. "Of course you feel uncomfortable when people you hardly know start laughing about a personal story from your past."

6. Display radical genuineness. This occurs when you truly understand what they are feeling on a deep level. Maybe this is because you have had this experience in the past. This empowers you to relate to their experience and to respond in the moment, on an equal footing with them. You might say, "Yeah, that sucks when you want to keep something private and someone shares it with others."

This validating exercise involves converting invalidating statements into validating ones. The first answer has been filled in. Hopefully, you can use some of these answers the next time you have an argument or tense situation you wish to sort out.

Validating Exercise

Practice on the empty "Validation" spaces. Follow the examples:

Situation:	
Your friend gets an A on an English essay and says, "I'm at the top of the class."	**Invalidation:** What BS. Jenny, Laura, and Stephanie always get higher grades than you. What makes you think you're so great?
	Validation: Congratulations on your excellent grade. You did a great job and are undoubtedly much smarter after studying for it
Situation: Friend's mad; you saw the movie they wanted with another classmate due to their parents' last-minute change of plans.	**Invalidation:** What are you, my owner? Don't I have the right to go out with other people without asking you along?
	Validation:
Situation: Your mom is mad because you said you'd tidy up your room a week ago, and it's still a mess.	**Invalidation:** Stop nagging me! I've been busy at school and with sports, and I'm tired!
	Validation:
Situation: Your sibling is disappointed because you told them you would help them with a math problem, and instead, you went to a friend's house.	**Invalidation:** Oh come on, learn your own stuff! Go on the Internet or something. I'm not your tutor.
	Validation:

Exercise 4: Reflections

The goal of reflection is to make you a good listener. When someone says something to you, you can validate them by repeating what they have said to you, but in your own words. Remember, doing so does not mean you agree with them fully or at all.

For instance, your best friend Nola is fuming because the teacher gave your group a poor grade for your science assignment:

> Nola: "I'm fuming! We worked so hard on that project and got a bad grade."

> You: "We did work very hard, so I totally get why you feel

1. Use a tone that expresses a bit of uncertainty. Your goal is to express, "I think this is what you want to say, but feel free to let me know if I've got it wrong."

2. Don't repeat the same phrase to reflect on what they are saying. Just a few statements you may want to try include:

   - "I hear you feeling like..."

   - "So you are saying that..."

   - "You are telling me that..."

Practice Reflections

How would you reflect these assertions from a friend?

1. "I was annoyed yesterday because the teacher gave us yet another surprise test. It's been one a day for the whole week!"

2. "I get worried when you don't text me back within a couple of hours."

3. "I don't get Melissa. First, she's chatty and friendly, and the next day, she hardly talks."

4. "I notice that it is almost always me who sends a text or calls you. If I don't make that move, then I won't hear from you."

5. "I feel kinda hurt that Micah didn't invite me to his sister's wedding when he invited everyone else in our friend group."

Exercise 5: What Is Your Communication Style?

We often speak about saying things assertively. Let's immerse ourselves a bit deeper into this topic. There are four main communication styles (Dialectical Behavior Therapy, n.d.):

1. **Assertive:** Assertive communication involves expressing your thoughts and emotions to others clearly without losing respect for others or yourself. When you are assertive, you pay attention to your needs and those of others and are good at making compromises (without saying "Yes" to everything and denying your own wants and needs).

2. **Passive:** Some people use this style because they fear others will dislike or reject them. People who use this style ignore their feelings and don't clearly state when something matters to them. They avoid giving an opinion that is different from that of others.

3. **Aggressive:** This style is intimidating. It involves putting your needs and goals first, regardless of the people around you. Sometimes, it is accompanied by yelling, swearing, and being verbally aggressive.

4. **Passive-Aggressive:** This style often involves ignoring others or ghosting them when they do something one doesn't like. People who use a passive-aggressive style do not express their emotions clearly but, rather, talk in a roundabout way. They tend to say "Yes" to others, even when they truly want to say "No." As a result, they can

Exercise:

1. From the above information, what is your predominant communication style?

2. With whom do you tend to use this style the most?

3. How effective is your communication style, and how does it affect you?

Exercise

The aim of this exercise is to differentiate between passive, aggressive, and assertive means of communication. Fill in the table to differentiate between passive, aggressive, passive-aggressive, and assertive communication styles. Before you start, here are five examples of assertive communication:

1. "I've been feeling frustrated about doing the dishes every day. I know you're busy, but I need your help. How can we do this fairly?"

2. "I know you wanted me to join you this weekend, but I don't stay over at places where parents aren't home. It's just a norm my parents expect me to follow."

3. "I'm having a hard time studying while you're playing on your phone. Could you kindly use your headphones while you're playing?"

4. "I'm sorry I can't drive you to the city tomorrow. I've been studying hard for exams and working at the coffee shop, and I need to rest."

5. "I know you aren't keen on Tommy, but he is my friend, and I do make it a point to spend time with him regularly. Maybe next time you can come along and get to know him more."

For instance:

SITUATION	Your friend wants to borrow your brand-new car to go on a date.
PASSIVE	"Okay, take it." (Even though you are super worried inside and absolutely do not want to lend it).
AGGRESSIVE	"Get lost, Eddie. As if I'd lend you my car. This took me years of weekend work to buy. You'll probably crash it or scratch it. No way!"
PASSIVE-AGGRESSIVE	"Okay, Eddie, you can have it. I'll bring you the keys on Friday." (Friday comes, and you don't show up to school, so you don't have to see him. You turn your phone off so you can't read his texts).
ASSERTIVE	"Eddie, we're good friends, and I'd love to help you out, but I don't lend my car to anyone. Sorry, it's a non-negotiable for me."

Sample 1:

SITUATION	Your friend wants you to ride in a car with someone who doesn't have a license.
PASSIVE	
AGGRESSIVE	
PASSIVE-AGGRESSIVE	
ASSERTIVE	

Sample 2:

SITUATION	Your friend wants you to ride in a car with someone who doesn't have a license.
PASSIVE	
AGGRESSIVE	
PASSIVE-AGGRESSIVE	
ASSERTIVE	

Sample 3:

SITUATION	Your parents want you to pursue a certain career path, but you're passionate about something else.
PASSIVE	
AGGRESSIVE	
PASSIVE-AGGRESSIVE	
ASSERTIVE	

Sample 4:

SITUATION	You are struggling with a subject in school, but you've never asked the teacher for help.
PASSIVE	
AGGRESSIVE	
PASSIVE-AGGRESSIVE	
ASSERTIVE	

Sample 5:

SITUATION	You are invited to a party where you know there will be underage drinking or other risky activities going on.
PASSIVE	
AGGRESSIVE	
PASSIVE-AGGRESSIVE	
ASSERTIVE	

Sample 6:

SITUATION	Your classmates frequently copy your homework, and it's starting to bother you.
PASSIVE	
AGGRESSIVE	
PASSIVE-AGGRESSIVE	
ASSERTIVE	

III: Self-Respect Effectiveness

Exercise 6: FAST

This exercise has one main aim: To empower you to maintain respect for yourself during a discussion or argument. FAST stands for:

Be **F**air

No **A**pologies

Stick to your Values

Be **T**ruthful

Before starting on this exercise, it pays to ask:...

What are your goals during a discussion?
They might be:

⇒ I want to act in a way that is consistent with my values and beliefs. (In other words, I won't give in just to end a discussion quickly if it means being untrue to my values.)

⇒ I will act in a way that makes me feel confident, capable, and effective.

⇒ I will act in a way that makes me feel happy about

Exercise 7: Exploring Your Values

This exercise aims to help you explore your values—so you can live by them and be your authentic self. Values are often passed by your family and your society, but you are always free to formulate your own. Fill in the table in accordance with what you know (Therapist Aid, n.d.). You will find one example for each box.

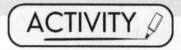

Exploring Your Values
ACTIVITY

My mom's values:	My dad's values:
1. Be honest.	1. Be forgiving.
2.	2.
3.	3.
4.	4.
5.	5.
The values of someone I respect:	**Society's values:**
1. Be creative.	1. Make lots of money.
2.	2.
3.	3.
4.	4.
5.	5.
The values I'd like to guide me:	**The values I actually live by:**
1. Be courageous.	1. Be safe and do what is expected of me.
2.	2.
3.	3.
4.	4.
5.	5.

Exercise 8: Value Discussion Questions

This exercise also attempts to help you define and live by your values. They comprise general questions to ask yourself and think about (Therapist Aid, n.d.).

1. Did you have values as a child that changed in your teen years?

2. What values do you have that are different from those of your friends, family, and your social setting?

3. What strength or quality do you most admire in others?

4. Which qualities in people do you dislike?

5. Which value have you not used in a while? How do you think you can incorporate it into your life more actively?

6. We show our values differently depending on the situation. How do you think your parents would describe your values? What about your friends? Your teachers? Your siblings? What facts would they base their opinions on?

CONGRATULATIONS!!

You have achieved the coveted
Tsavorite of Connection.
Put it on a poster or keep it in your wallet as
a reminder of the superpower you have just
discovered: interpersonal effectiveness!
You've come such a long way! You can
assert your wants and needs, establish
boundaries, respect yourself, and resolve
arguments and conflicts with others.
You'll receive a certificate of your Tsavorite
of Connection. This will be a forceful
reminder of the power within you that can
harness to build meaningful, long lasting
relationships!

Scan to receive

CELEBRATORY ACTIVITY:

A Mindfulness Meditation Session with your Tsavorite in the treehouse on Leopard Hill

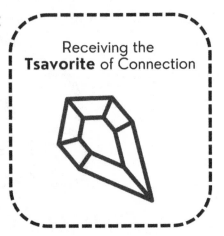

Receiving the **Tsavorite** of Connection

Welcome to this mindfulness meditation session, which will take place in the beautiful treehouse on Leopard Hill. Today, we will embark on a journey of connection and exploration, seeking the metaphorical Tsavorite of Connection within ourselves. As we dive deeper within ourselves, we will discover the kindness, empathy, and understanding that help us build close connections with others.

Sit or lie down in a comfortable spot, close your eyes, and take a deep breath. Inhale to the count of five, then exhale to the count of seven. Visualize yourself walking into the treehouse, surrounded by the lush trees and overlooking the beautiful wildlife below. The swaying trees create a sense of tranquility, and the roof of the treehouse keeps you cool and calm as you get ready to connect with your inner world.

The stars are shining in the sky above, and a stunning full moon rises above the home.

Become aware of your body, scanning it from your toes all the way up to your head to notice any areas of tension or discomfort. As you exhale, release any tension that has built up, letting it go with each breath.

Next, shift your focus to your emotions. Recognize any emotions you may be experiencing at this moment. Whether it's happiness, anger, elation, or frustration, accept these feelings without judgment or the need to change them.

With a sense of inner calm, explore the art of assertiveness. Let go of any fears or anxieties that may arise when thinking about expressing yourself assertively.

Take a deep breath, and as you exhale, repeat in your mind or out loud:

"I have the right to express what I want and need assertively."

"I can do so clearly and respectfully."

Now, think about a situation or a conversation where you'd like to express yourself more assertively. Picture yourself calmly and confidently expressing your needs. Visualize the other person responding positively to your assertiveness and validating you.

Recognize that validation is essential in every interaction. Just as you wish to be heard and understood, others also need to know that their feelings are real and important to you.

With this in mind, take another deep breath, and as you exhale, say:

"I honor the feelings and thoughts of others."

"I listen to them with empathy, and I do not judge them."

"I validate the emotions of those around me, even if I disagree with them."

Take a moment to think of a scenario where you might encounter a disagreement or difference of opinion. See yourself responding with kindness and respect, reflecting on someone's words without judging them.

As we come to the end of this practice, remind yourself that assertiveness, validation, kindness, and respect are powerful tools for building strong, meaningful relationships. Carry these principles with you in your daily life.

You are feeling calm, and your Wise Mind is in action. And as you look around the treehouse, you notice a green, sparkly gem resting on a cushion. This gem is the Tsavorite of Connection. Its vibrant green color represents the heart chakra, signifying love, compassion, and communication.

Pick up the Tsavorite and hold it gently in your hand. Take a moment to observe its deep green hue, appreciating its unique beauty, just like the connections you have with your loved ones—each one is unique and priceless. As you hold this gem, its radiant energy fills you with a sense of warmth and appreciation for all the meaningful connections in your life. Carry its verdant beauty in your heart, approaching others with kindness and understanding and remembering to be kind to yourself, too.

SECTION 4

CHAPTER 8

Distress Tolerance: How to Strengthen Your Mind Against the Toughest Challenges

GEM: The Diamond of Resilience

"Radical acceptance rests on letting go of the illusion of control and a willingness to notice and accept things as they are right now, without judging."

MARSHA M. LINEHAN

Your aim in Section 4 (Chapters 8 and 9) is to find the Diamond of Resilience by discovering resilience: a skill that will help you stand tall, even in the face of strong emotional challenges. In this chapter, you will discover how DBT can help you ride through tough emotions and swim to the shore afterward. In Chapter 9, you will get straight to work, completing a series of exercises and worksheets so you can practice what you've learned.

The Diamond of Resilience

In the introduction, we mentioned that resilience isn't about dodging curveballs or pretending that life doesn't hurt sometimes. Instead, it's about bouncing back when things go wrong, and kids, teens, and adults all benefit from getting up, dusting themselves off, and moving on, learning something important from challenging experiences. This chapter will focus on how you can withstand distressing situations by employing key strategies, some of which change your body chemistry.

Where Is the Diamond? Visiting Cova des Mirador in Ibiza

The magnetic island of Es Vedrà is a famous mass of rock sitting in the middle of the Mediterranean Sea. Many believe that it is the third most magnetic point on the planet. They believe that its summit holds a high concentration of energy that could attract aliens. Standing at 385 meters above sea level, this rock

Scan to see the magnificient location

The Diamond of Resilience

Diamonds are, quite simply, the hardest material in the world! They can only be scratched by something of equal or greater hardness. In other words, only a diamond can scratch another diamond.

It, therefore, makes sense that diamonds are often given as special gifts. They are sturdy, so you know they will last forever. What's more, they are a shining symbol of everlasting love. But for DBT purposes, diamonds are the ultimate symbol of resilience.

seems to rise out of the water and is an undeniably beautiful site to behold at sunset.

Legend has it that the Greek hero, Ulysses, was lured from the deck of his ship and enhanced by the seduced song of the sea sirens in the waters surrounding this island. Another story has it that a priest, Father Don Francisco Palau, was confined in Ibiza in the 1850s. He took refuge in a cave in Es Vedrà to meditate and had powerful mystical visions there.

To find this diamond, you will travel to Cova des Mirador, a tiny cavern directly below the main Es Vedrà viewpoint that gazes out on Ibiza's most enigmatic islet. Within this cavern, there is a hidden gap halfway down the left side of the cave. There, wrapped in silk cloth, is the Diamond of Resilience. Remember that the diamond is an emblem of perfection and invincible spiritual power. It is a symbol of light, brilliance, and an unconquerable spirit. It is a powerful reminder that your mind has the strength and resilience to overcome even the toughest and most distressing emotions.

What Is Distress Tolerance?

Distress tolerance is one of DBT's four sections. It can be defined as a person's ability to manage an emotional incident without feeling overwhelmed. It is the quality that enables you to return to your normal state when stressors arise.

What Things Are Distressing You?

A distressful event can arise unexpectedly and cause a very quick chain of emotions to arise. However, things can seem a lot more

The Cova des Mirador in Ibiza

Es Vedrà, a magnetic island in the Mediterranean, believed to be the planet's third most magnetic point. It is shrouded in mystique. Its summit, at 385 meters above sea level, allures with its undeniable beauty, especially at sunset.

painful, difficult, or tiring if you are already stressed. Everyone has their own set of circumstances and stressors, but some of the main sources of distress for teens (according to a recent APA survey) include the pressure to achieve academically, the culture of perfection, and negotiating the sometimes tough and competitive world of social media.

Perfectionism Can Hurt

In the documentary Race to Nowhere, director Vicky Abeles— whose daughter became physically ill as a result of homework, school, and extracurricular activities—talks about how damaging perfectionism can be. Her documentary challenges current thinking about how society prepares teens for success. She argues that in order to break the cycle of stress and unhealthy behaviors, teens should be provided with better support and health education at school and at home, as well as at the community level and via interactions with health care professionals (Jong, n.d.).

Some of the most powerful current teen stressors include (Visions Teen 2023)

- juggling responsibilities such as school, work, and sports.
- having problems with friends
- peer group pressure
- bullying
- comparing oneself to others on social media
- changing schools or moving to another city or town
- seeing their parents undergo divorce or separation
- financial problems in the family

- financial problems in the family
- having negative thoughts about themselves
- physical changes
- anxiety or depression
- the death of a family member

In addition to long-term stressors, you may also go through events that cause immediate distress. These events can really put you to the test. They can result in rumination (thinking the same thoughts over and over again in your mind), anguish, depressive thoughts, and anxiety. They can leave you feeling hopeless like there is nothing you can do to get out of a painful situation.

If you feel like this, know that it is only human. As a teen, you want to fit into your friend group and get on with your teachers and classmates. You also want to understand what is expected of you, do well academically, and enjoy the thrill of being part of a group or team. Below is a small list of events that can cause sudden, intense hurt, testing your

- arguments with friends at school
- being left out of social occasions with friends
- being "rejected" by someone you have a crush on
- being teased at school
- being put down by a teacher or a classmate
- being scolded or punished for something you didn't do
- getting a bad grade on an exam
- an upcoming test or project
- not making a sports team at school
- not winning a competition
- being put down by a sibling

Distress tolerance can make these events much more bearable, so practicing these skills is one of the best investments you will make in your own health and happiness. **The benefits of distress tolerance include:**

1. You'll be able to survive an emotional problem without making it worse.
2. You won't lose your cool, bridges aren't broken, and you won't regret your actions later.
3. You'll cope with your feelings, especially when you don't know exactly what you want or need at a given moment.

What Skills are Involved in Distress Tolerance?

Some of the most important distress tolerance skills DBT can help you with include (Compitus 2020):

- **Self-Soothing Techniques:** These can be used to calm yourself down when you are feeling distressed. Think of a child and the way they sometimes soothe themselves with their favorite blanket, stuffed toy, or dummy. DBT techniques can serve the same purpose as these objects of comfort.

- **Resetting Your System Using TIPP Skills:** TIPP is an acronym for Temperature, Intense Exercise, Paced Breathing, and Paired Muscle Relaxation. These skills calm the limbic system and lower your state of emotional arousal very quickly, and they can be a powerhouse when things get really challenging!

- **The STOP Skill:** This skill stops you from acting on impulse.

Skills that Involved in Distress Tolerance

Some of the most important distress tolerance skills DBT can help you with include (Compitus 2020):

Self-Soothing Techniques

Resetting Your System Using TIPP Skills

The STOP Skill

Pros and Cons

Radical Acceptance

Distraction

Improving the Moment

- **Pros and Cons:** When you are in a crisis situation, the typical behavior is to act with the emotional mind instead of the wise mind. By weighing the pros and cons of saying or doing something, you can avoid making decisions you will regret.

- **Radical Acceptance:** Life often throws obstacles in your way, as it tends to do for everyone. Imagine if, instead of fighting against the pain they cause, you accepted them radically, with no holds barred! "This is the way it is" is one of the most powerful statements you can make to yourself.

- **Distraction:** When all else fails, do something that distracts you! Don't sit passively stewing in negativity. When things are getting so tense that you think you can't bear it, take a break from the distressing situation and get back to it when you can deal with it calmly. Distraction is NOT repression. It is just a break that you can take during particularly tough emotional times.

- **Improving the Moment:** This technique focuses on taking the edge off difficult or intense moments. The technique suggests many possible skills, including

You may not be able to avoid hard knocks altogether, but you have all the power you need to stop them from leading you to destructive thought patterns and behaviors. Are you ready to feel the island of Es Vedrà's powerful magnetic force and find the Diamond of Resilience?

CHAPTER 9

Complete the Distress Tolerance Challenge

PRIZE: The Diamond of Resilience

"No life is not worth living. But what is important is that you experience your life as worth living—one that is satisfying, and one that brings happiness."

MARSHA M. LINEHAN

You are getting closer to finding the last DBT gem, but before you do so, let's take a look at a few statistics that show why knowing how to handle distressful thoughts and emotions is so important:

⇒ *A national survey on drug use and health has found that around 13 percent of teens aged 12 to 17 said they had experienced at least one major depressive episode in the previous year.*

⇒ *Americans aged 15-29 and 30-49 have the highest stress levels, 64 percent, and 65 percent, respectively. Worry is also high in both age groups, standing at 50 percent and 52 percent, respectively (The American Institute of Stress 2022).*

⇒ *At age 13, about 8 percent of U.S. teens have a diagnosable anxiety disorder. By 18, up to 15 percent of all teens experience symptoms of a clinical anxiety disorder.*

For many people, DBT has proven to be no less than a lifeline when they are feeling at their lowest. Remember that DBT is based on two main pillars: self-acceptance and the adoption of skills that can better equip you to deal with the thoughts and emotions that can contribute to anxiety, depression, and other issues. Each of the exercises below is aimed at helping you boost your resilience.

I: Self-Soothing

Exercise 1: Self-Soothing Worksheet

The goal of this worksheet is to identify the activities that work for you when you are feeling emotionally overwhelmed or even out of control. When you feel this way, it means the emotional part of your brain is taking over, and the rational part of your brain is subdued. By calming your emotions, you can help your brain produce "feel-good hormones" that help you feel better and get out of a negative spiral of emotions (Between Sessions 2014).

When choosing activities, bear in mind that the following factors make them more soothing:

- **Familiarity:** Sometimes, memories from our past can evoke positive emotions. For instance, a specific fragrance or food may remind you of a happy time in your childhood—one you spent with someone you love.

- **Multi-Sensory:** Our emotional brain responds best when we engage in activities that involve our five senses. For instance, walking in the forest can stimulate the senses of sight, sound, touch, smell, and even taste (if you know how to forage safely).

- **Repetitive Motions:** Research shows that repetitive motion (such as knitting, playing the piano, or rocking in a chair) can also produce feel-good hormones. This is why some people pace back and forth when they are stressed.

This exercise invites you to choose:

⇒ *activities you can undertake when you are starting to feel overwhelmed*

⇒ *those you can undertake before a situation you think might stress you out*

⇒ *those you can do regularly to practice managing your emotions (The more you practice, the easier it will be to self-soothe when a distressing situation arises.)*

Below is a list of activities you can do IMMEDIATELY when emotions are threatening to get the better of you. You can choose from these suggestions or explore your own ideas.

- Walk backward and forward.
- Sit in a green area like a park.
- Take five long breaths.
- Chew gum.
- Sip on a cup of herbal tea.
- Do a dance routine.

Activities you can do BEFORE a situation you know will be emotionally draining.

- Meditate.
- Breathe.
- Smell essential oils like lavender or citrus oils.
- Knit.

- Cook.
- Listen to music.

Activities you can do REGULARLY to boost your self-soothing skills.

- Bathe and groom your pet.
- Read.
- Rock in a chair for 10 minutes.
- Care for a garden.
- Do some outdoor yoga or stretching.
- Cycle outdoors.

Now, use the following worksheet to score the activities you choose from 1 to 10.

Activity Rating Exercise

Use the following worksheet to score the activities you chose from 1 to 10.

For Example:

Activity	Date undertaken	Rating (1-10)	Thoughts about this activity
Meditation	14th October 2023	8	I was feeling very anxious before heading to a party. I meditated for half an hour before I left and felt much more relaxed afterward.

Activities Rating Exercise
PRACTICE

Activity	Date undertaken	Rating (1-10)	Thoughts about this activity

Exercise 2: Self-Soothe With Your Five Senses

Write down five ways you can soothe yourself by using each of your senses (Linehan 2014). Examples are provided in the table below.

For Example:

Sight	Sound	Smell	Taste	Touch
star-gazing, looking at photographs, watching the flame on a candle flicker	listening to a calming song, listening to birds chirp, listening to white noise	smelling a scented candle, diffusing essential oils in my room, spraying myself with a perfume that uplifts me	eating your favorite snack, trying out ice-cream flavors, chewing your favorite gum	petting your dog, having a massage, hugging a family member

Practice:

Sight	Sound	Smell	Taste	Touch

II: Changing Your Brain Chemistry Using TIPP Skills

TIPP stands for:

*T*emperature

*I*ntense Exercise

*P*aced Breathing

*P*aired Muscle Relaxation

As you will see, each of the letters stands for something you can do to alter your brain chemistry and calm down when you are distressed. An important thing to remember is that these exercises can be unsafe for people with heart conditions, as well as those who take some types of medication (such as beta blockers), and people who struggle with eating disorders or have temperature intolerance. If you are in doubt or have any of these issues, speak to your doctor first (DBTSelfHelp.com, n.d.).

TIPP Works in The Following Way:

- Temperature: Cooling your body down is a shortcut to a calm state. You can do this by taking a short, cold shower, placing an ice pack on your face and neck, placing your face in a sink or bowl filled with cold water, or holding ice and watching it melt. Apply cold in 30-second stints, as you don't want to get too cold or damage your skin. While you are undertaking these activities, try to harness your Wise Mind to calm you down further.

- Intense Exercise: Working out intensely can help you move out of a difficult emotional state. You can try exercises like sprinting, cycling, or swimming. Once again, try to access your Wise Mind so you don't push your body too hard.

- Paced Breathing: The aim of this exercise is for you to control your breathing and to bring your breathing rate down. Count to five as you inhale and to seven as you exhale. Focus on your breath and notice how slow breathing almost immediately lowers your heart rate. This is why this exercise is so powerful if you are prone to anxiety attacks.

- Pair It With Muscle Relaxation: Breathe in and tense your belly up (without causing a cramp), then let your belly relax as you breathe out. Notice the difference between keeping your muscles in a tense state and relaxing them.

Exercise 3: Choose One TIPP Exercise to Try

Simply try out one of the above exercises when you feel stressed this week. Reflect on which were most effective and write down how they made you feel in your journal.

III: Harness the STOP Skill Instead of Acting on Impulse

STOP is an acronym for:

Stop: Do not react.

Take a step back: When you feel distressed, take a break from the situation, practice some breathing, and simply let go.

Observe: What's happening in and around you? What are you thinking and feeling? What are others doing?

Proceed mindfully: Tap into your Wise Mind before moving forward.

You can also add an "R" into the equation:

Remember your goals: What actions will help you achieve them? What actions may stand in their way?

Exercise 4: Try the STOP Technique

Try this technique out at least once this week. Jot down how well it worked for you and compare it to the other distress tolerance exercises in this chapter. Which soothed you the fastest? Which had the longest-lasting effect? Which did you feel most comfortable doing? For instance, if a classmate says something hurtful to you, you can:

Stop: Don't react, even if you are tempted to answer them back quickly.

Take a step back: Simply walk past and head outside if you can. While you are there, practice some controlled breathing, or listen to a short mindfulness script.

Observe: Keep your mind on exactly what is taking place around you. For instance, you might observe some children playing in the background, notice flowers growing near where you're sitting, or take notice of how the school is decorated.

Next, you can **Proceed Mindfully,** perhaps deciding to go back into class and concentrate on the tough math problems your teacher is explaining that day.

You can also remember your goals. On this particular day, it may be to stay calm and not give into others' provocations.

IV: Weighing the Pros and Cons

Exercise 5: Why Tolerate Your Distress

In this exercise, simply weigh the pros and cons of tolerating vs. not tolerating distressful emotions.

For Example:

PROS	CONS
I can "ride the waves of difficult emotions" and reduce the intensity of my emotions.	I have to practice these skills because I am not used to them.
I can feel badly about life for a much shorter period, then connect with others and do the things I love.	My body and mind are telling me to wallow in my emotions.

Practice:

PROS	CONS

V: Radical Acceptance

Radical acceptance is one of the fundamental tenets of DBT. It encourages you to accept that life is tough and that you can feel powerful urges to do yourself harm without actually giving into these urges. You don't have to pretend that the pain and urges don't exist, but it does help to take this energy and use it to formulate a strategy that will keep you moving forward.

Exercise 6: Radical Acceptance Worksheet

Take your journal and read the following questions, answer them, and reflect on your answers a few days later. This is one worksheet you can use every time you feel overwhelmed by a situation (Positive Psychology, n.d.):

1. What situation or event made you feel distressed? What happened?

```
                                                                

                                                                

                                                                

                                                                

                                                                
```

2. What past events led up to this situation or event?

```
                                                                

                                                                

                                                                

                                                                

                                                                
```

3. How were you involved in the development of the situation?

4. How were others involved in its development?

5. What part of this situation did you have control over?

6. What part were you NOT in control over?

7. How did you respond to the situation?

8. How did this response make you feel?

9. How do you think it made others feel?

10. How could you have reacted or responded differently?

11. If you had fully and radically accepted the situation, how would the outcome have been different?

Exercise 7: Problem-Solving

This exercise harnesses the 7-step problem-solving method to help you focus on solutions instead of negative emotions. If you find you are overthinking a problem and getting more and more upset, empower yourself by deciding that you will take steps to fix it. Take your journal and go through each of the 7 steps:

1. Identify the problem.
2. Brainstorm various solutions.
3. Weigh the pros and cons of each of the above solutions.
4. Choose one solution and write down the exact steps to carry it out.
5. Try it out.
6. Reflect on whether it worked. If not, what aspects went wrong, and what different solution could you try next time?
7. Even if the problem wasn't solved, did you achieve even a little progress? Did you learn anything from applying this method?

Exercise 8: Make Your List of Radical Acceptance Coping Mantras

Positive affirmations can put you into a positive mindset and help you realize that you manage your emotions, not the other way around (Positive Psychology, n.d.). You can use the following mantras. Try to come up with around five of your

- This is how things are.
- I can't undo what happened.
- Everything is exactly as it should be based on past events.
- I cannot predict the future.
- I cannot control other people.
- I will not always agree with others, and that's okay.

VI: Distraction

Sometimes, the best way to get out of a distressful state of mind is to choose a distraction to focus on. To complete this exercise, select from the following list of distracting activities the next time you think you might benefit from having a break from your thoughts and emotions. Feel free to add your own ideas to the list!

To remember the items, think of the saying, Wise Mind ACCEPTS (Linehan 2015).

ACCEPTS stands for:

 for **"ACTIVITIES"**

- Watch a film or series.
- Tidy up your room.
- Go out to eat with a friend.
- Read a page-turning book.
- Play a computer game online with friends.

 for **"CONTRIBUTING"**

- Raise funds for a cause.
- Go on a beach clean-up or park clean-up day.
- Plant a tree.
- Do something nice for someone working in public service.
- Make a gift for someone.

 for **"COMPARISONS"**

- Compare how you are feeling now to how you felt at a different time.
- Compare yourself to someone who is having a harder time instead of someone who seems to "have it all."
- Watch a true-life story about someone who has had a challenging life.
- Read a book on someone who has overcome great strife.
- Think about people who have coped with a similar situation to the one you are facing.

for *"EMOTIONS"*

- Listen to uplifting music.
- Watch an emotionally charged film.
- Read a book that is about emotions.
- Watch a scary or funny movie.
- Listen to a funny podcast.

 ## for *"PUSHING AWAY"*

- Let a situation go and resolve to get back to it later.
- Build an imaginary wall between yourself and the issue.
- When you are overthinking or going over the same thoughts again and again, shout, "No!"
- Avoid the problem for just one moment or day.
- Put your problem in a box for just one moment or day.

 ## for *"THOUGHTS"*

- Solve a mystery.
- Do a puzzle or play a mental game.
- Play Wordle.
- Try to recall the lyrics of a song.
- Try to remember a soliloquy from a famous play.

 ## for *"SENSATIONS"*

- Go out into the rain.
- Have a relaxing bath.
- Hold ice in your and watch it melt.
- Squeeze a stress ball.
- Listen to loud music.

VII: Improve the Moment

This skill involves relying on each of the letters in this acronym to make a difficult moment a bit easier to bear (Greene 2020).

IMPROVE is an acronym for:

- **Imagery:** Imagine something that makes you feel safe, happy, and calm. For instance, you might imagine that you are on the shore of a beautiful beach with crystalline waters or dream up your own colorful world!

- **Meaning:** When things are tough, try to focus on and do things that give your life meaning. For instance, you might enjoy walking the dogs at a shelter, doing something kind for the police officers or firefighters in your area, or visiting someone who is old or lonely.

- **Prayer:** Some people find praying to a higher power for strength very useful. Others simply enjoy feeling connected to something that is greater than themselves. For others, simply tapping into their Wise Minds can feel like a type of prayer.

- **Relaxing Actions:** Try to think of the things you love to do at the end of a tired day or when you are feeling tightly wound up. Your list can include playing tennis, going for a run, painting, designing artwork on your tablet, taking a bath with bath bombs and essential oils, or meditating.

- **One thing in The Moment:** Try to focus on one thing well instead of "everything, everywhere, all at once." When you feel stressed or low, thinking of past regrets or future worries can make it all worse. Try to remain "in the here and now," using some of the techniques you picked up in the Mindfulness section of this book.

- **Vacation:** Enjoy a quick break. You don't have to book a flight to the Bahamas to benefit from taking a pause. Your break can involve going for a swim, watching your favorite Netflix show, or having a massage.

- **Encouragement:** Be your own cheerleader when times are tough. Give yourself courage with affirmations like "I can do this," "I have risen to similar challenges in the past," or "This is tough, but it won't last forever."

Exercise 8: Improve Your Moment

Choose a specific situation you find distressful or that you found distressful in the past. Think about how you can apply each of the IMPROVE skills to help you cope. An example of how you can use each of the IMPROVE skills can be found below:

- Imagery: Imagine that you are in the place you vacation with your family.

- Meaning: Do something nice for someone in school who isn't in your friend group and who you don't often talk to.

- Prayer: Some people enjoy opening the Bible or another sacred scripture randomly, reading the spot their finger lands on!

- Relaxing Actions: Why not read your favorite comic book or manga to relax? How about listening to BTS, your favorite hip-hop artist, or another band?

- One thing in The Moment: For instance, make a

collage that represents your friendships or family life, and take time to concentrate fully on creating a beautiful, colorful work you can share with your loved ones after.

- Vacation: You may not be able to go to your favorite vacation spot yet, but how about heading to the gym for a Zumba class, or creating a new TikTok choreography with your best friend?

- Encouragement: Tell yourself, "I am enough, just the way I am."

IMPROVE YOUR MOMENT
YOUR TURN

IMAGERY

MEANING

PRAYER

RELAXING ACTIONS

ONE THING IN THE MOMENT

VACATION

ENCOURAGEMENT

CONGRATULATIONS!

Embrace the priceless
Diamond of Resilience
you've earned. Carry it through
life's journey, confident in your
ability to conquer all challenges,
illuminating the path forward with
your inner strength and
determination.
There's an award waiting for you.
You'll receive a certificate of
your diamond as a powerful
reminder of how resilient you
are, even against the greatest
challenges.

Scan to receive

CELEBRATORY ACTIVITY:

A Mindfulness Meditation Session with your Diamond in Cova des Mirador

Receiving the
Diamond of Resilience

Welcome to this guided meditation for resilience, where we will tap into the strength of the Diamond of Resilience, found in a hidden crevice in Cova des Mirador, overlooking the magnetic islet of Es Vedrà in Ibiza.

Sit or lie down in a comfortable spot, close your eyes, and take a deep breath. Inhale to the count of five, then exhale to the count of seven. Release any tension in your body as you exhale and scan your body from your toes to your head, letting go of accumulated stress. Allow yourself to be fully present in this moment.

Now, visualize a sparkling diamond in your mind's eye. This diamond symbolizes the immense strength that resides within you. Picture its facets reflecting the light, shimmering and radiating fire and light.

You find yourself walking into the stunning Cova des Mirador. You enter into its welcome shade and gaze out at the sea and at the imposing islet of Es Vedrà. The gentle breeze carries the scent of the sea, filling your senses with peace.

You take a few steps into the cave, and its mysterious beauty enraptures you. Your eye is caught by a hidden crevice halfway down the left side of the cave. There, wrapped in silk cloth, is the Diamond of Resilience.

Approaching the diamond, you gently pick it up and hold it in the palm of your hand. As you do so, you feel an incredible surge of energy flow through your entire being. It's like nothing you have felt before. You are illuminated from head to toe, and you feel a surge of strength take over you. The diamond is a reminder that you have an unbreakable spirit. You are capable of overcoming any challenge, obstacle, or problem that comes your way.

Take a moment to reflect on the obstacles you've faced in your life and the strength you've displayed in overcoming them. Acknowledge the role that all your ups and downs have played in making you the strong yet kind person you are today.

Now, imagine the diamond merging with your heart, infusing you with its brilliant fire. You are now one with the essence of resilience. As you breathe in and out, let the diamond remind you that you are strong, capable, and resilient in the face of adversity.

Take a few moments to sit in stillness, absorbing the diamond's energy and allowing it to illuminate every cell of your body. Embrace your ability to rise above challenges, just like the diamond that stands as a symbol of strength and endurance.

When you are ready, slowly open your eyes, bringing this sense of strength with you into your daily life. Remember that the diamond's power resides within you at all times. You can call upon it whenever you need a reminder of your resilience.

Carry this newfound sense of resilience with you as you navigate life's journey, knowing you can overcome anything that comes your way. Embrace the challenges as opportunities for growth, and let the Diamond of Resilience within you shine brightly, lighting up the path ahead.

SPREAD THE WORD...

If this book has helped you manage your emotions, get on with others, and get through distressing situations more confidently, please leave a review on Amazon.

Share your thoughts on the most powerful components of DBT—and let others know how the strategies in your book helped you ride through the pain and come out stronger on the other side.

WANT TO HELP OTHERS?

Thank you for your support. I look forward to someone reading your words and feeling inspired to transform their life through self-acceptance and goal-oriented change.

Scan the QR Code to leave your rating/review on Amazon.

CONCLUSION

Congratulations on meeting this book's four challenges and finding the Ruby of Protection, the Sapphire of Emotion, the Tsavorite of Connection, and the Diamond of Resilience. My hope is that you can take these symbolic gems wherever you go, relying on the different DBT strategies from this book in your day-to-day life, as well as when you are facing a particularly tough emotional challenge.

Many therapies can help you view life in a more positive light, but when it comes to managing your emotions, DBT is definitely one of the most powerful. Earlier, I spoke of Marsha M. Linehan and the fascinating story of how DBT was developed. I mentioned that Marsha fought many brave battles of her own, surviving many suicide attempts before discovering her own pearl of wisdom: sometimes you can't avoid pain. Trying to escape from pain or pretending it doesn't exist won't help. In fact, it will make it worse, leading you to let out your sadness, frustration, and anger through behaviors that can be hurtful to yourself and others.

In Chapter 2, we talked about mindfulness and why it is so powerful when it comes to "riding through waves of emotion." By keeping your mind in the here and now and accepting your emotions non-judgmentally, it becomes easier to understand that your emotions are not permanent. Good and bad emotions come and go. What's more, your emotions do not define you. You can feel angry or fearful, for instance, without being an angry or fearful person. In Chapter 3, you took part in mindfulness and grounding exercises and practiced what it is like to let your Wise Mind be your guide when the going gets tough.

Of course, mindfulness is just one part of DBT. Marsha Linehan espoused that you need to accept and validate yourself and your emotions and take active steps to change the things you can so you can enjoy a more fulfilling life. This is where the next three sections come in handy.

Chapter 4 introduced you to emotional regulation strategies that help you define, describe, and manage your emotions instead of passively allowing them to take over. In Chapter 5, you discovered techniques that can help you identify your emotions, set goals, and develop an awareness of the cognitive distortions that can lead you to see situations in a far more negative light than is necessary.

You also saw that sometimes, doing the opposite of what your urges are telling you can be a powerful strategy to stop a tense situation from getting out of hand. You also learned the value of pausing to acknowledge your emotions, give yourself permission to feel them, and exercise self-understanding to avoid making things harder on yourself than they already are.

The third section, covered in Chapters 6 and 7, is centered on building healthy, fulfilling relationships with others. You saw that doing so involves being kind and empathetic to others and being true to yourself. You don't have to say yes all the time or allow others to overrun your boundaries just to get on with others. In fact, relationships are always stronger when both parties respect each other's boundaries and are willing to negotiate and compromise when necessary.

In Chapters 8 and 9, you covered the final section: distress tolerance. You learned that even when things are at their most heated, you can take a break for a while and get back to the situation later. You also worked out how to change your body chemistry so you can immediately (and quite dramatically) calm down and lower your heart rate when you are feeling distressed.

Know that it is only logical and expected for you to find some DBT challenges harder to complete than others. For instance, if you are prone to overthinking or worrying about the future, then you may find mindfulness difficult to master when you first start. Keep at it! The rewards are immeasurable! You don't have to allow triggers caused by people or situations to lead you to a state of panic or sadness. You can stand up for yourself, calm yourself down, and obtain strength from the knowledge that even the most painful and difficult moments pass.

Please use this book as a companion—one that you return to often. Do the exercises and worksheets many times over. One day is not the same as the next, and every situation is different. Get used to journaling daily, if possible. Write your thoughts down and review what you wrote a few days, weeks, and/or months later. You will probably find that you have made great progress, which will inspire you to rely on the practical, powerful strategies you have learned in this book throughout your lifetime.

Download the meditation scripts at the end of every section and play them when you are working on the section they belong to.

Get the meditation audios here.

The Ruby of Protection, the Sapphire of Emotion, the Tsavorite of Connection, and the Diamond of Resilience are all there for you to hold and connect with. Let them remind you that you are far more resilient, flexible, and capable of growth than you ever imagined!

Something for you...

Each meditation corresponds to a section of this book. Empower your yourself while enjoying moments of calm and reflection.

Scan the QR Code below to download your copy.

TEENS

ARE *Missing*

ESSENTIAL SKILLS

BEYOND

text books

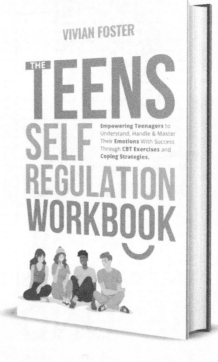

HELP
Teens
Manage their
EMOTIONS
—— and ——
OVERCOME
STRESSORS

S T O P
MISSING OUT
just because you are

SHY

Discover a new
CONFIDENT YOU

TAKE BACK

CONTROL

— OF YOUR —

ANGER

help your children

THRIVE IN LIFE

HELP
YOUR CHILD
TRANSFORM
into the person

THEY TRULY ARE

REFERENCES

American Gem Society. "July Birthstone: History of Rubies." Accessed July 1, 2023. https://members.americangemsociety.org/page/rubyhistory

Attai, Khobi. "DBT: The Emotional Mind, the Rational Mind, and the Wise Mind." Living Well Counselling Services. December 1, 2020. https://livingwellcounselling.ca/dbt-emotional-mind-rational-mind-wise-mind/

AZ Quotes. "Marsha M. Linehan Quotes." Accessed July 1, 2023. https://www.azquotes.com/quote/765854

Between Sessions. "Learning to Self-Soothe." Accessed July 1, 2023. https://www.betweensessions.com/wp-content/uploads/2014/09/Learning_to_Self_Soothe.pdf

Bray, Suzette. "Emotion Regulation in Dialectical Behavior Therapy." Good Therapy. March 18, 2013. https://www.goodtherapy.org/blog/emotion-regulation-dialectical-behavior-therapy-dbt-0318135

Carey, Benedict. "Expert on Mental Illness Reveals Her Own Fight." The New York Times. June 23, 2011. https://www.nytimes.com/2011/06/23/health/23lives.html

Cherry, Kendra. "Emotional intelligence: How we perceive, evaluate, express, and control emotions." Verywell Mind. May 2, 2023. https://www.verywellmind.com/what-is-emotional-intelligence-2795423

Cleveland Clinic. "Dialectical Behavioral Therapy (DBT)." Accessed July 1, 2023. https://my.clevelandclinic.org/health/treatments/22838-dialectical-behavior-therapy-dbt

Cognitive Behavioral Therapy Los Angeles. "Mindfulness from a DBT Perspective." Accessed July 1, 2023. https://cogbtherapy.com/cbt-blog/mindfulness-in-dbt

Competus, Katherine. "What Are Distress Tolerance Skills? Your Ultimate DBT Toolkit." Positive Psychology. October 1, 2020. https://positivepsychology.com/distress-tolerance-skills/#:~:text=A%20person's%20ability%20to%20manage,%2C%20%26%20Tull%2C%202011)

CRAFT Connect: SHARE & SELF-CARE GROUP. "Finding Our Wise Mind - Spiral Staircase Exercise Session." Accessed August 15, 2023. https://static1.squarespace.com/static/5ecb35369d9c412a9d920761/t/60f64e5fd18f246b0cf05614/1626754655048/06.Wise+Mind-Spiral+Staircase.7.13.21.pdf

Creative Healing Philly. "6 Levels of Validation and Why They Work." January 5, 2021. https://creativehealingphilly.com/blog/6-levels-of-validation-and-why-they-work

Davison, Peter. "Swashbuckling Geologist Who Mined a

Sparkling Seam." Financial Times. August 29, 2009. https://www.ft.com/content/e482eed6-9404-11de-9c57-00144feabdc0

DBTSelfHelp.com. "Awareness Exercises." Accessed August 12, 2023. https://dbtselfhelp.com/dbt-skills-list/mindfulness/how-skills/

DBTSelfHelp.com. "Emotional Regulation." Accessed August 12, 2023. https://dbtselfhelp.com/dbt-skills-list/emotion-regulation/#:~:text=Emotion%20Regulation%20is%20the%20Dialectical,and%20build%20positive%20emotional%20experiences.

DBTSelfHelp.com. "Factors Reducing Interpersonal Effectiveness." Accessed August 12, 2023. https://dbtselfhelp.com/dbt-skills-list/interpersonal-effectiveness/factors-reducing-interpersonal-effectiveness/

DBTSelfHelp.com. "How Skills: One-Mindfully, Non-Judgmentally, Effectively." Accessed August 12, 2023. https://dbtselfhelp.com/dbt-skills-list/mindfulness/how-skills/

DBTSelfHelp.com. "Relationship effectiveness: GIVE." Accessed August 12, 2023. https://dbtselfhelp.com/dbt-skills-list/interpersonal-effectiveness/give/

DBTSelfHelp.com. "TIPP: Changing Your Body Chemistry." Accessed August 12, 2023. https://dbtselfhelp.com/dbt-skills-list/distress-tolerance/tipp/

Dialectical Behavior Therapy. "Communication Styles." Accessed August 12, 2023. https:// dialecticalbehaviortherapy.com/interpersonal-effectiveness/ communication-styles/

Dialectical Behavior Therapy. "E1: Recognizing Your Emotions." Accessed August 12, 2023. https:// dialecticalbehaviortherapy.com/emotion-regulation/ recognizing-your-emotions/

Dialectical Behavior Therapy. "E2: Being Effective." Accessed August 12, 2023. https://dialecticalbehaviortherapy.com/ emotion-regulation/being-effective/

Dialectical Behavior Therapy. "E7: Emotion Exposure." Accessed August 12, 2023. https:// dialecticalbehaviortherapy.com/emotion-regulation/emotion -exposure/

Dialectical Behavior Therapy. "M8: Wise Mind." Accessed August 12, 2023. https://dialecticalbehaviortherapy.com/wp -content/uploads/2020/04/DBT-Forms-M8-Wise-Mind.pdf

Edström, M. "Son Doong 360: Exploring the World's Largest Cave." National Geographic. Accessed August 10, 2023. https://www.nationalgeographic.com/news-features/son-doong-cave/2/#s=pano52

Greene, Paul "DBT: IMPROVE the Moment — How to Make Crises Bearable." July 27, 2020. Manhattan Center for Cognitive Behavioral Therapy. https://

www.manhattancbt.com/archives/1699/dbt-improve-the-moment/

Guy-Evans, Olivia. "Fight, Flight, Freeze, Or Fawn: How We Respond To Threats." Simply Psychology. July 21, 2023. https://www.simplypsychology.org/fight-flight-freeze-fawn.html#:~:text=Fight%3A%20facing%20any%20perceived%20threat,please%20to%20avoid%20any%20conflict.

Guy-Evans, Olivia. "Primary and Secondary Emotions: Recognizing the Difference." Simply Psychology. June 13, 2023. https://www.simplypsychology.org/primary-and-secondary-emotions.html

Hall, Karyn. "Self-Respect in Relationships." National Education Alliance for Borderline Personality Disorder. May 19, 2021. https://www.borderlinepersonalitydisorder.org/self-respect-in-relationships/#:~:text=Self%2Drespect%20effectiveness%20is%20the,met%2C%20and%20maintain%20your%20relationship

Hartney, E. "10 Cognitive Distortions That Can Cause Negative Thinking." November 15, 2022. Verywell Mind. https://www.verywellmind.com/ten-cognitive-distortions-identified-in-cbt-22412

Holmes, Lindsay. "10 Great Things That Happen When You Set Boundaries." HuffPost. April 12, 2016. https://www.huffpost.com/entry/setting-boundaries-benefits_n_57043126e4b0b90ac27088bb

Huppert, Felicia A. and Daniel M. Johnson. "A Controlled Trial of Mindfulness Training in Schools: The Importance of Practice for an Impact on Well-Being." The Journal of Positive Psychology 5, no. 4 (August 2010): 264-274. https://doi.org/10.1080/17439761003794148

Jelinek, Joslyn J. "What Is Emotional Dysregulation?" PsychCentral. (November 21, 2022). https://psychcentral.com/blog/what-is-affect-or-emotion-dysregulation

Kaiser Permanente. "Mindfulness Handout 4B." Accessed July 19, 2023. https://mydoctor.kaiserpermanente.org/ncal/images/Mindfulness%20DBT%20Skills%20ADA_05012020_tcm75-1599005.pdf

Lam, Julia W. Y.. (2017, June 20). "The Wandering Mind: How the Brain Allows Us to Mentally Wander to Another Time and Place." Frontiers. June 20, 2017. https://kids.frontiersin.org/articles/10.3389/frym.2017.00025#:~:text=For%20example%2C%20mind%20wandering%20in,problems%20or%20other%20negative%20experiences

Linehan, Marsha M. (2014). DBT (R) Skills Training Handouts and Worksheets. 2nd ed. Guilford Publications.

Long, Valerie. "Teens' Stress Is Higher Than Ever." Childrens Resource Group. Accessed July 18, 2023. https://www.childrensresourcegroup.com/crg-newsletter/stress-anxiety/teens-stress-higher-ever/

Lorandini, Jeanette. "Opposite Action for Overwhelming Emotions: How to Make it Work for You." Suffolk DBT. Accessed July 4, 2023. https://suffolkdbtjl.com/opposite-action/#:~:text=Opposite%20action%20is%20a%20dialectical,we'd%20rather%20not%20make.

Martin, Sharon. "7 Types of Boundaries You May Need." PsychCentral. April 23, 2020. https://psychcentral.com/blog, imperfect/2020/04/7-types-of-boundaries-you-may-need

Morgan, Aabey. "The Importance of Interpersonal Skills in the Workplace." One Education. August 4, 2021. https://www.oneeducation.org.uk/importance-of-interpersonal-skills-in-the-workplace/

National Institute of Mental Health. "The Teen Brain: 7 Things to Know." Accessed June 14, 2023. https://www.nimh.nih.gov/health/publications/the-teen-brain-7-things-to-know#:~:text=The%20brain%20finishes%20developing%20and,prioritizing%2C%20and%20making%20good%20decisions.

Nemours Kids Health. "Sleep and Your Teen." Accessed July 2, 2023. https://kidshealth.org/en/parents/sleep-problems.html#:~:text=The%20body%20releases%20the%20sleep,for%20bed%20before%2011%20p.m.

Nemours Teen Health. "Common Sleep Problems." Accessed July 13, 2023. https://kidshealth.org/en/teens/sleep.html#:~:text=During%20the%20teen%20years%2C%20the,a%20harder%20time%20falling%20asleep.

Positive Psychology. "Radical Acceptance Coping Mantras." Accessed August 4, 2023. https://positive.b-cdn.net/wp-content/uploads/2020/10/Radical-Acceptance-Coping-Mantras.pdf

Positive Psychology. "Radical Acceptance of a Distressing Situation." Accessed July 18, 2023. https://positive.b-cdn.net/wp-content/uploads/2020/10/Radical-Acceptance-of-a-Distressing-Situation.pdf

Quote Fancy. "Top 10 Marsha M. Linehan Quotes." Accessed June 24, 2023. https://quotefancy.com/marsha-m-linehan-quotes

Raes, Filip, James W. Griffith, Katleen Van der Gucht, and J. Mark G. Williams. "School-Based Prevention and Reduction of Depression in Adolescents: A Cluster-Randomized Controlled Trial of a Mindfulness Group Program." Mindfulness 5, no. 5 (March 2013): 477-86. https://doi.org/10.1007/s12671-013-0202-1.

Raising Children. "Moods: Helping Pre-teens and Teens Manage Emotional Ups and Downs." Accessed July 20, 2023. https://raisingchildren.net.au/pre-teens/mental-health-physical-health/about-mental-health/ups-downs

Schimelpfening, Nancy. Dialectical Behavioral Therapy (DBT): Definition, Techniques, and Benefits. May 1, 2023. Verywell Mind. https://www.verywellmind.com/dialectical-behavior-therapy-1067402#toc-what-is-dbt-used-for

Self-Help Toons. "DBT Mindfulness "How" Skills and "What" Skills." Accessed July 4, 2023. https://www.selfhelptoons.com/dbt-mindfulness-how-skills-what-skills/#:~:text=There%20are%20three%20%E2%80%9Cwhat%E2%80%9D%20mindfulness,involve%20how%20we%20practice%20mindfulness.

Skills You Need. "Interpersonal Skills." Accessed August 18, 2023. https://www.skillsyouneed.com/interpersonal-skills.html

Smith, Amanda. "16 Inspiring and Thoughtful Quotes from Marsha Linehan." Hope for BPD. Accessed September 1, 2023. https://www.hopeforbpd.com/borderline-personality-disorder-treatment/quotes-about-dbt#:~:text=Sometimes%20we%20cannot%20change%20the,you%20will%20change%20your%20emotions.

Tang, D. F., L. Q. Mo, X. C. Zhou, J. H. Shu, L. Wu, D. Wang, & F. Dai. (2021, December 23). "Effects of Mindfulness-Based Intervention on Adolescents Emotional Disorders: A Protocol for Systematic Review and Meta-Analysis." Medicine 100, no. 51. https://doi.org/10.1097/MD.0000000000028295

Tara Arnold Inc. "Dialectical Behavior Therapy: Interpersonal Effectiveness Overview." (Accessed July 27, 2023). https://taraarnoldinc.com/interpersonal-effectiveness#:~:text=There%20are%20three%20goals%20of,%2C%20and%20self%2Drespect%20effectiveness

Tasmanian Suicide Prevention Community Network. "Mindfulness Handout 2." Accessed August 2, 2023. https://

www.suicidepreventiontas.org.au/__data/assets/
pdf_file/0003/254145/mindfulness_-_Wise_Mind.pdf

The American Institute of Stress. "Stress in Teens." April 6,
2022. https://www.stress.org/teens

Therapist Aid. "Cognitive Distortions." Accessed July 5, 2023.
https://www.therapistaid.com/worksheets/cognitive-
distortions

Therapist Aid. "DEAR MAN." Accessed July 5, 2023. https://
www.therapistaid.com/worksheets/dbt-dear-man

Therapist Aid. "Exploring Values." Accessed July 5, 2023.
https://www.therapistaid.com/worksheets/exploring-values

Therapist Aid. "Reflections Communication Skill." Accessed
July 5, 2023. https://www.therapistaid.com/worksheets/
reflections-communication

Therapist Aid. "Value Discussion Questions." Accessed July 5,
2023. https://www.therapistaid.com/worksheets/values-
discussion-questions

Tsavorite. "Campbell Bridges." Accessed July 5, 2023. http://
www.tsavorite.com/history/campbell-bridges.html#:~:text=%
2C%20%E2%80%9CTanzanite%E2%80%9D.-,Mr.,and%20in%
20Kenya%20in%201970.

Vaughn, Stephanie. "Validation in DBT: Basics and Purpose."
Psychotherapy Academy. Accessed July 5, 2023. https://
psychotherapyacademy.org/section/basics-of-validation/

Visions Teen. "4 Causes of Teenage Stress." April 18, 2022. https://visionsteen.com/4-causes-of-teenage-stress/

Wilding, Melody. "Emotional labelling: How to Control Stress and Feel Less Anxious by Naming Emotions." Accessed July 14, 2023. https://melodywilding.com/control-stress-and-feel-less -anxious-with-emotional-labelling-free-toolkit/ #:~:text=Studies%20show%20that%20naming%20your,for% 20what%20to%20do%20next

World Health Organization. "Mental Health of Adolescents." Accessed July 19, 2023. https://www.who.int/news-room/fact -sheets/detail/adolescent-mental-health

Thomas, S. (2022, May 25). *The best Shakespeare quotes about love*. London Theatre. https:// www.londontheatre.co.uk/theatre-news/news/the-best- shakespeare-quotes-about-love

Video References:

Oxalis Adventure https://www.youtube.com/watch?v=FJH_nnlrMol

Pinoy Travel Freak Vlog https://www.youtube.com/watch?v=nqNylDdm2ys

Visma https://youtu.be/w89Zd3xn_IQ?si=vFkphF-_dlqEzsHA

Made in the USA
Coppell, TX
23 May 2024

32686118R00135